# Statistics in Linguistics

# Statistics in Linguistics

*Christopher Butler*

Basil Blackwell

© C. S. Butler 1985

First published 1985

Basil Blackwell Ltd
108 Cowley Road, Oxford OX4 1JF, UK

Basil Blackwell Inc.
432 Park Avenue South, Suite 1505,
New York, NY 10016, USA

*British Library Cataloguing in Publication Data*

Butler, Christopher
    Statistics in linguistics.
    1. Linguistics – Statistical methods
    I. Title
    410'.1'5195    P138.5
    ISBN 0-631-14264-9
    ISBN 0-631-14265-7 Pbk

*Library of Congress Cataloging in Publication Data*

Butler, Christopher
    Statistics in linguistics.
    Bibliography: p.
    Includes index.
    1. Linguistics – Statistical methods. I. Title.
    P138.5.B87   1985   410'.2'8   85-3885
    ISBN 0-631-14264-9
    ISBN 0-631-14265-7 (pbk.)

Typeset by Unicus Graphics Ltd, Horsham, West Sussex
Printed in Great Britain by Billings Ltd, Worcester

# Contents

# Preface

In language study, as in the natural sciences, sociology or psychology, many kinds of work require the collection of quantitative data. The literary stylistician may wish to count the relative numbers of various colour terms, tense forms, alliterative sounds or some other linguistic feature of the texts in which he is interested. The language teacher or course designer may wish to obtain and compare measures of students' performances under two teaching methods. The theoretician may wish to count how many words in a corpus of texts occur once, how many twice and so on, and to compare these observed data with those predicted by a theoretical model of vocabulary distribution in texts. These are just a few examples of the many possible kinds of quantitative investigation into language. In all of them, we need ways of making sense of the data, and this is the purpose of statistical methods.

In many quantitative studies, we cannot investigate every possible example of the phenomenon we are interested in. In some cases exhaustive investigation is *theoretically* impossible; for example, if we were studying the time taken by informants to utter a particular sentence, the number of possible readings is infinite. In other cases, exhaustive examination is theoretically possible but impracticable; for instance, if we were examining some phonological feature of the English spoken in Birmingham, we could in theory obtain data from every Birmingham resident (or, better, from every resident satisfying a set of predetermined criteria for qualifying as a 'Birmingham speaker'); but this would be extremely time-consuming and difficult to organise, so that we should almost certainly be content with a *sample* from the total population we are concerned with. One important part of statistics is concerned with methods of sampling, and with the relationships between measurements made on samples, and the properties of the populations these samples are intended to represent.

Once we have a set of data, either for every occurrence of our chosen phenomenon or for a sample of it, we usually need to summarise it in such a way that we can discern its general characteristics. The tools available for this task constitute *descriptive statistics*. Presented with a long list of numbers representing our observations, it is often not easy to see, at a glance, any general trends in the data. Such trends become more obvious when we look at the distribution of the data. For instance, in a language proficiency test on 100 learners, we might record marks out of 20. We can determine how many learners score 0, how many score 1, how many 2 and so on, up to 20, thereby drawing up a *frequency distribution* for the data, which may be converted to graphical form, and which gives an indication of the most typical score as well as the spread of marks. More precise measures of these properties can be obtained by performing certain statistical calculations on the data.

Very often, we are concerned not with the characteristics of just one set of data, but with the comparison of two (or more) sets. For example, we might be interested in testing the hypothesis that the performance of two groups of learners, taught by different methods, will differ in a language proficiency test; or we may wish to investigate whether the proportions of two pronunciations differ in the casual and formal speech of informants. In such cases we face the problem of designing our study in such a way that it will isolate just those phenomena we wish to test. The samples we use must be chosen so as to minimise variation arising from unwanted complicating factors, so that we can be reasonably confident that any effects owing to our chosen phenomenon are not swamped by other, 'irrelevant', effects. Experimental design is, or should be, inseparable from statistical work: no amount of sophisticated statistics can compensate for a badly designed investigation.

Where comparisons are involved, we need to know not only the general characteristics of each sample (such as the most typical value and the spread of values) but also whether the characteristics of the two samples are sufficiently different for us to conclude that there is a real effect that is due to the factor we are investigating. We can never be absolutely sure that a difference between two sets of observations has not arisen 'by chance', owing to inherent variability in our material. We can, however, carry out tests which may allow us to claim 'real' differences with a specifiable margin of error, say 5 per cent, or 1 per cent, or 0.1 per cent. That is, we may, as a result of our calculations, claim to be 95 per cent sure, or 99 per cent sure, or even 99.9 per cent sure, that we have found a 'real' difference. This area, known as *hypothesis testing*, is an important part of *inferential statistics*.

In summary, then, whenever we wish to collect quantitative data on language, we need to pay careful attention to the design of our study, and to the selection of appropriate statistical methods for summarising the data, and for testing hypotheses concerning differences between sets of data. All these aspects of statistics are discussed in this book. However, since the book is introductory in scope, some techniques of interest to linguists, such as multiple correlation and regression, cluster analysis, and analysis of variance with more than one independent variable, are excluded. In order to deal adequately with these more advanced techniques, at least one further volume would be required.

Many courses on applications of statistics concentrate far too heavily on the methods themselves, and do not pay sufficient attention to the reasoning behind the choice of particular methods. I have tried to avoid this pitfall by discussing the 'why' as well as the 'how' of statistics. A difficult problem for the writer of any text on mathematical topics for non-mathematicians is how far to go into the derivation of formulae. While recognising that most linguists (including myself) will have neither an interest in the more theoretical side of the subject nor the mathematical background necessary for a full discussion, I feel that it is highly unsatisfactory for readers or students simply to be presented with a formula, with no explanation whatever of how it is arrived at. Where I thought it appropriate, I have attempted to give an idea of the rationale behind the various methods discussed in the book. Nevertheless, readers should find that their school arithmetic and algebra will see them through quite easily.

I should like to express my thanks to the various groups of students who have worked through the material presented here, and to Tim Gibson, who checked many of the exercises. My thanks go also to the following, for permission to use copyright or unpublished material:

Statistical tables in appendix 1: Dr H. R. Neave and his publishers George Allen & Unwin, for original or adapted versions of tables

x   *Preface*

2.1(a), 3.1, 3.2, 3.3, 5.1, 5.3, 6.2, 6.4 and 7.1 from *Statistics Tables for Mathematicians, Engineers, Economists and the Behavioural and Management Sciences* (1978); question 7 of chapter 9 exercises: Dr J. Connolly, for data from his article, 'Quantitative analysis of syntactic change', *Nottingham Linguistic Circular* 8/2, 108–18 (1979); question 6 of chapter 9 exercises: Dr J. Coates and Professor G. Leech, for data from their article, 'The meanings of the modals in modern British and American English', *York Papers in Linguistics* 8, 23–34 (1980); question 4 of chapter 11 exercises: Professor G. Wells and the publishers of *Research in Education*, for data from the article, 'Language use and educational success: a response to Joan Tough's *The Development of Meaning* (1977)', *Research in Education* 18, 9–34; questions 2 and 3 of chapter 2 exercises, question 3 of chapter 3 exercises, question 5 of chapter 9 exercises, questions 1 and 3 of chapter 10 exercises: Dr A. S. Crompton, for data from his work on stress and pause in French.

I should also like to thank Professor D. Crystal for advice on the production of the book.

# 1 Some fundamental concepts in statistics

## 1.1 Introduction

In this chapter, some ideas of fundamental importance in statistics are introduced. We first consider the concepts of population and sample. We then differentiate between the two broad areas of statistical investigation: descriptive and inferential statistics. Finally, we consider some important ways in which statistical variables can be classified.

## 1.2 Populations and samples

In everyday speech, the term 'population' is normally taken to mean a collection of human, or at least animate, entities, as in 'the population of Greater London', or 'the rat population of the London sewers'. In statistics, however, the term is used more generally, to refer to any collection of entities, of whatever kind, that is the object of investigation. Thus, we may speak of the population of words in a given text, the population of nouns in Dickens's *David Copperfield* or the population of measurements of the time taken to utter a particular sentence on different occasions. It is with the characteristics of populations, or aggregates of individual entities, that statistics is most fundamentally concerned.

We may draw a distinction between *finite* and *infinite* populations. The population of nouns in *David Copperfield* or of past historic verbs in Camus's *La Peste* is finite: the number of entities is fixed and countable. Other kinds of population, however, are potentially infinite: in theory, at least, we could repeat our measurement of utterance times for a sentence an infinite number of times.

With a finite population which is not too large, we may be able to investigate the whole population. But if our population is potentially infinite, or if it is finite but very large, we shall have to be content with *samples* drawn from the population concerned. The use of samples, even for the study of finite populations, cuts down the labour and cost involved in obtaining results, and mini- mises the errors which can easily be made during the processing of large amounts of statistical data. Let us imagine that we are interested in the acceptability judgements of native speakers of Parisian French when presented with a series of French sentences. Clearly, it would be impossible, in practice, to use every speaker of Parisian French as an informant (quite apart from the considerable difficulties involved in deciding what counts as 'Parisian French'). Instead, we take a sample of the speakers concerned, in the hope that our results will be generalisable to the population of such speakers as a whole.

Clearly, great care must be exercised in selecting samples if generalisation to the population is to be valid. Statistical methods of inferring the properties of populations from those of samples are based on the assumption that the samples are *random*. This does not mean that they are chosen in a haphazard manner: rather, it means that every unit in the population has an equal chance of being represented in the sample.

In order to select a truly random sample from a finite popula- tion, we need to have a complete list of the units in the population (often called the 'sampling frame'). Each unit in the sampling frame is allocated a number. One way of doing this is to put into a box a set of paper slips, each bearing a number, from 1 to the total size of the population, mix up the slips thoroughly, and withdraw a number of slips equal to the desired sample size. This method, though simple, is tedious, and a rather better way is to use a table of random numbers, in which the digits 0 to 9 are arranged in a very long sequence, in random order. Sets of statis- tical tables incorporating such information are readily available, and an excerpt from one such table is given as table A1 of appendix 1. The digits are grouped into fives, but this is merely for con- venience in reading. Let us imagine that we wish to draw a sample of 50 lines of poetry from a text containing 800 lines. Since our population size is 800, a three-digit number, we need to take groups of three digits from the table of random numbers. We may begin anywhere in the table; for convenience, let us start with the first three digits in column 1 of table A1. Reading down the column, we select items 494, 294, 252, 24, 694, 772 and 528 as the first seven 'members' of our sample. The next two figures are 987 and 850, which are too large for our population of 800, so we ignore them. The next members of the sample are lines 177, 637, 616, 422, 452, 403, 540, 491, 76, and so on.

A variation of simple random sampling is known as *systematic* or *quasi-random* sampling. Here, we decide the first unit in the sample by truly random methods, and then take units at equal intervals throughout the numbered population, the intervals being chosen to give the desired number in the final sample. Let us consider again the selection of a sample of 50 lines of poetry from a text of 800 lines. Our sampling interval will be 800/50, or 16. We choose some point in the random number tables, and find the first two-digit combination which is smaller than or equal to 16. If this was, say, 12, we should take lines 12, 28, 44, 60, 76, and so on, up to and including line 796. Such a sample is not truly random, because the second and subsequent units are not chosen independently of the first. This does not matter seriously, provided that there is no periodicity in the population such that units with certain properties tend to recur at regular intervals. For instance, if the work of a particular prose writer showed a rather regular sentence length of about 20 words, and the sampling interval for selection of a sample of words from his work was also 20, the sample might contain a preponderance of words from the beginnings or ends of sentences, and this might seriously affect the representativeness of the sample.

A variation within systematic sampling is *block sampling*, where the position of the beginning of the sample is determined randomly, but the next *N* items are taken, where *N* is the size of the sample. For instance, in selecting 500 words from a text of 10 000 words, one might start at word 4 581 (determined from random number tables), and take words 4,581 to 5 080 inclusive. The chances of such a passage being unrepresentative are considerable, and obviously vary according to the nature of the population and its structure.

It is important to realise that the selection of a sample by methods designed to achieve true randomness (such as using a table of random numbers) does not guarantee that the sample arrived at will indeed be representative of the population. Consider, for example, the selection of a sample of ten people from the adult population of a village for linguistic testing, and assume, for simplicity, that there are equal numbers of men and women in the village. To calculate the chances of getting various possible mixes of men and women in the sample, we must make a short digression into elementary probability theory.

To simplify matters still further, let us first consider the selection of just three people from the village adult population. Since there are equal numbers of men and women, the probability that the first person selected will be a man is 0.5 (as is also, of course, the probability that this person will be a woman). Now, the laws of probability state that the probability of two independent events both occurring is equal to the product of the probabilities of the individual events. So the chances of both the first and the second members of our sample being men (or of both being women) is 0.5 × 0.5, or 0.25, and the probability of all three being men (or all being women) is 0.5 × 0.5 × 0.5, or 0.125. Now let us look at the possibility of getting two men and one woman in our sample. There are three ways in which this could happen:

| Sample member no. | 1 | 2 | 3 |
|---|---|---|---|
| | man | woman | man |
| | man | man | woman |
| | woman | man | man |

The probability of each of these outcomes is 0.125, so that the total probability of getting two men and one woman is 3 × 0.125, or 0.375. Similarly, we can get two women and one man in any of three ways:

| Sample member no. | 1 | 2 | 3 |
|---|---|---|---|
| | woman | man | woman |
| | woman | woman | man |
| | man | woman | woman |

Again, the total probability is 0.375. We thus arrive at the situation shown in table 1.1. (Actually, this is an oversimplification, since the simple theory holds good only if each unit selected is put back into the population before the next choice is made, and this is clearly not possible in our situation, as we must avoid the possibility of the same person being chosen twice. This can, however, be ignored for our present purposes, provided that the

**Table 1.1**

| Outcome | Probability |
|---|---|
| 3 men | 0.125 |
| 2 men + 1 woman | 0.375 |
| 2 women + 1 man | 0.375 |
| 3 women | 0.125 |

population is large in relation to the sample size.) Note that the probabilities add up to 1.000, as indeed they must.

We could go through the same kind of reasoning for more complicated cases, but fortunately there is a general formula which will save us this trouble. If $p$ and $q$ are the probabilities of two mutually exclusive, independent events (such as choosing a man and choosing a woman, in our example), then the possible outcomes of $n$ selections are determined by expanding the formula $(p+q)^n$. For the case where $n = 2$, we have

$$(p+q)^2 = p^2 + pq + pq + q^2 = p^2 + 2pq + q^2.$$

For $n = 3$, we have

$$(p+q)^3 = (p+q)(p^2 + 2pq + q^2)$$
$$= p^3 + 2p^2q + pq^2 + qp^2 + 2pq^2 + q^3$$
$$= p^3 + 3p^2q + 3pq^2 + q^3.$$

For the case where $p=q=0.5$, the terms evaluate to $0.125+0.375 +0.375 +0.125$, and this is the result we obtained from first principles above. This type of distribution is known as the *binomial distribution*. We shall not discuss it further here: details can be found in any comprehensive statistics textbook (see, for example, Ferguson 1981).

We may now return to our original problem: predicting the probabilities of various outcomes in the selection of ten people from our village population. If the probabilities are worked out for $n = 10$, using the expansion discussed above, we obtain the results shown in table 1.2.

The reader will remember that the point of this digression was to enable us to see just how representative of the population a

Table 1.2

| Men | Women | Probability |
|-----|-------|-------------|
| 0 | 10 | 0.001 |
| 1 | 9 | 0.010 |
| 2 | 8 | 0.044 |
| 3 | 7 | 0.117 |
| 4 | 6 | 0.205 |
| 5 | 5 | 0.246 |
| 6 | 4 | 0.205 |
| 7 | 3 | 0.117 |
| 8 | 2 | 0.044 |
| 9 | 1 | 0.010 |
| 10 | 0 | 0.001 |

randomly selected sample of ten people might be. Ideally, we should like the proportion of men and women in the sample to reflect that in the population: that is, five men and five women. We see from the above that the probability of just this outcome is about a quarter (to be more precise, 0.246). The chances of getting eight or more men in the sample (or, of course, eight or more women) are 0.044 + 0.010 + 0.001, or 0.055 – that is, over 1 in 20. Putting this another way, if we took 20 samples of ten people from the village, we could expect one of these to contain eight or more men, and one to contain eight or more women. Such a sample would hardly be representative of the sex distribution of the village. Furthermore, it is not hard to see that any types of unit which have a small overall proportion in the population may well not be represented in the sample at all.

One way to minimise this problem is to select a sample by *stratified random sampling*. If the proportions of various subgroups in the population are known, then random sampling can be undertaken within each stratum, and the resulting subsamples combined to give an overall sample. For example, in selecting a sample of ten adults from our village, we might choose, by random methods, five men and five women, and combine the two subsamples. Such a procedure would be an example of *proportional* stratified random sampling, since the proportion of men and women in the final sample is the same as in the population. As a further example of proportional stratification, consider the problem of selecting a sample that will be as representative as possible

**Table 1.3**

|  | Early period | Middle period | Late period |
|---|---|---|---|
| Novels | 500 000 | 700 000 | 300 000 |
| Short stories | 100 000 | 200 000 | 200 000 |

of the range of an author's literary prose works. Let us assume that the author's total output of 2 million words is divided into genres and periods as in table 1.3. We might then choose our sample so that 500 000/2 000 000, or 0.25 of it, came from early novels, 700 000/2 000 000, or 0.35, from middle novels, and likewise 0.15 from late novels; 0.05 from early short stories, 0.1 from middle-period short stories, and 0.1 from late short stories. Within each of these categories, we could select our subsample by simple random sampling, or by systematic or even block sampling methods.

A stratified framework has an additional advantage in that it allows comparisons to be made between subsamples corresponding to the various groupings. This is possible with a proportionally stratified sample such as those discussed above. Often, however, the optimum situation for comparison of subgroups is one in which these subgroups are of equal size, despite their unequal proportions in the population as a whole. A sample chosen in this way is said to be a *disproportionally* stratified sample. Imagine, for instance, that we wish to select a sample of 120 000 words from the 2 million word output of our hypothetical author. Table 1.4 compares the number of words taken from each subgroup under (1) proportional and (2) disproportional stratified sampling.

If we wish to use the results from a disproportionally stratified sample to estimate the properties of the population as a whole, we must obviously give the various strata different weightings. For instance, there are only two-thirds as many words from early novels in the disproportional sample as in the proportional sample, so that we should weight by a factor of 3/2, or 1.5, the contribution of the results from this subgroup; and so on.

We should also mention *multi-stage sampling*, which, as the term suggests, consists of sampling by successive stages, treating the sample at one stage as the population for the next. For example, if we wished to obtain a sample of 100 pages from the

Table 1.4

|  | Proportional | Disproportional |
|---|---|---|
| Novels |  |  |
| Early | 30 000 | 20 000 |
| Middle | 42 000 | 20 000 |
| Late | 18 000 | 20 000 |
| Short stories |  |  |
| Early | 6 000 | 20 000 |
| Middle | 12 000 | 20 000 |
| Late | 12 000 | 20 000 |

novels of Dickens, we might first select five novels by a random procedure, using the total set of novels as the population, and then within each novel select 20 pages, again at random. Sometimes, investigations which at first sight look as if they are based on single-stage sampling are in fact better regarded as multi-stage. Consider the situation where we wish to select two samples from a class of language learners, in order to compare the effectiveness of two different teaching methods. The samples chosen for comparison are samples of the class taken as a population; but we should probably want to try to generalise from that particular class of learners to the whole population of learners of similar characteristics, at a similar stage of development.

This last point brings us to an important practical issue. We have seen that true random sampling from a finite population requires the listing of the entire population. It is often impossible, or at least impracticable, to obtain a list of the whole population in which we are interested. In some cases of sampling involving human populations, electoral and similar lists can be useful; but even here, we must be careful not to use, as a sampling frame, a list that has some in-built bias which might prejudice our results. A list of telephone subscribers, for example, would almost certainly bias our sample towards the middle and upper ranges of the social class scale. In many cases, we have to make do with a 'population' which is 'given' by some practical circumstance, such as the members of a school, or even a class within a school. In such cases, if we wish to generalise beyond that group we must, if possible, do our best to demonstrate that the properties of the group do not differ radically from those of the population in which we are really interested. For instance, we might try to show that the distribution of ages, sexes, IQ ratings and social classes in a particular school is not too far removed from the norm for schoolchildren in the country as a whole. Often, however, the norm itself is unknown and difficult to determine; furthermore, it may not always be clear just what factors are relevant. We must therefore be on our guard against the understandable temptation to claim greater generalisability for our results than is warranted by the situation.

Finally in this section, we must introduce two more technical terms connected with populations and samples. The properties of populations are normally called *parameters*, while the properties of samples from populations are called *statistics* (or sometimes *estimates*). Imagine that we select 1 000 words randomly from a text of 50 000 words, and find that their mean (a kind of 'average') length is 3.54 letters. This measure is a statistic for the sample, and is used as an estimate of the true population parameter, which probably will not be exactly 3.54 letters. Fortunately, as we shall see, methods are available for assessing the degree of confidence we may have in the reliability of such estimates. Statistics are normally symbolised by Roman letters (for instance, $\bar{x}$, read as 'x-bar', for the mean of a sample), while parameters have symbols consisting of Greek letters (such as $\mu$, 'mu', for the mean of a population).

## 1.3 The descriptive and inferential functions of statistics

In the preface to this book, a distinction was made between the *descriptive* and *inferential* functions of statistics. We shall now examine this distinction in rather more detail, by means of a practical illustration.

Let us suppose that we have selected two samples of 30 language learners each, one taught by traditional methods, the other by means of the language laboratory. We have given both groups a proficiency test in the target language, with the following results:

*Class A* (language laboratory): marks out of 20:
15, 12, 11, 18, 15, 15, 9, 19, 14, 13, 11, 12, 18, 15, 16, 14, 16, 17, 15, 17, 13, 14, 13, 15, 17, 19, 17, 18, 16, 14.

*Class B* (traditional): marks out of 20:
11, 16, 14, 18, 6, 8, 9, 14, 12, 12, 10, 15, 12, 9, 13, 16, 17, 12, 8, 7, 15, 5, 14, 13, 13, 12, 11, 13, 11, 7.

Before we can make very much sense out of these data, we need to summarise their important properties. We might, for example, construct a table showing the number of students in each group who gained 0, 1, 2, 3, 4, 5 marks, and so on up to 20 (that is, a *frequency distribution* table). We should also want to know what the most typical, or 'average', mark is for each group, and how much variation there is in each set of marks. All these are ways of describing the data in a readily assimilable form, and one which will permit further statistical work. These areas of descriptive statistics are discussed in chapters 2 and 3 below.

However, we shall almost certainly want to go beyond the mere description of the data, important as this is. One piece of information we shall probably need is what degree of confidence we may have in extrapolating from our groups to any other similar groups taught by similar methods. Rephrasing this in terms of samples and populations, we wish to view our groups as samples from the entire hypothetical population of similar students who have been or could be taught by each of the two methods. We thus wish to use the measures made on our samples (sample statistics – for instance, the mean mark), in order to estimate the corresponding parameters for the populations concerned. The area of estimation is discussed in chapter 5, for which chapter 4 lays some essential groundwork.

A further piece of information we shall certainly want is whether it can be claimed that one of our groups has done better on the test than the other. We may, perhaps, postulate that the group taught by the language laboratory method will perform better than the group taught by the traditional method. Here we are concerned with the extremely important area of *hypothesis testing*. The basis of such tests, and its close relationship with the design of experimental investigations, form the subject of chapter 6, and the following chapters then discuss some of the more important tests available, their uses and limitations.

The areas of estimation and hypothesis testing both involve the inferring of relationships from descriptive measures: together, they constitute the area of inferential statistics.

## 1.4   Variables and their classification

Statistics is essentially concerned with *variable* quantities. In most investigations of a quantitative nature, we vary one or more sets

**Table 1.5**

| Independent variable | Dependent variable |
| --- | --- |
| Type of teaching method | Score on language test |
| Sentence complexity | No. of sentences recalled correctly by subjects |
| Social class | Percentage of -*ing* endings pronounced [ɪn] by subjects |
| Topic of newspaper article | Sentence length |

of conditions, and measure the effect on one or more properties of interest to us. The conditions that we ourselves vary are called *independent variables*, while those whose response we are measuring are *dependent variables*. Some examples of possible pairings are shown in table 1.5.

We may also distinguish between continuous and non-continuous (or discrete) variables. *Continuous variables* may take any value within a given range; for example, the time taken to utter a sentence is a continuous variable. *Discontinuous* or *discrete variables*, on the other hand, can take only certain values; for example, any given word may be 1, 2, 3, 4 letters long, and so on, but it may not be 1.5 or 2.61 or 3.141 59 letters long (although, of course, the mean length of a number of words is a continuous variable, and may take values such as 2.61).

A further important dimension of variable classification concerns the 'level of measurement' appropriate to the variable. Some variables are purely qualitative; in respect of such variables, entities may be the same or different, but not 'more' or 'less'. Variables of this kind are called *nominal variables*. As an example, take the occurrence of end-stopped lines in poetry: either a line ends in punctuation, and so is end-stopped, or it does not; there is no question of one line being more or less end-stopped than another. Likewise (if we assume, for the purposes of the discussion, that clear-cut assignments of parts of speech can be made), the part of speech of a given word in a particular sentence, or interpretation of a sentence, is a nominal variable: a word either can be classified as an adjective or it cannot.

With other variables, it may be possible to rank values on a scale of 'more or less'. Imagine, for example, that we ask a panel of informants to rate a set of sentences for 'acceptability' (defined in some precise way). The raters may well be able to say that sentence A is more acceptable than sentence B, which is in turn more acceptable than sentence C, and so on. In this case, acceptability would be an *ordinal variable*. A further example of an ordinal linguistic variable might be the politeness of particular forms of request or command in a given sociolinguistic situation.

With ordinal variables, it is not possible to claim that there are truly equal intervals between points on the scale of 'more or less'. For instance, one would probably not wish to claim that the difference between the acceptability of sentence A and that of sentence B was exactly the same as that between the acceptability of sentences B and C. With some variables, however, the so-called *interval variables*, such statements are possible. It is not easy to find examples of true interval variables in linguistics, so we shall take an everyday phenomenon instead. We can say that temperatures of 10 °C and 20 °C differ by the same amount as 20 °C and 30 °C, or 30 °C and 40 °C. We can, therefore, say that temperature is an interval variable.

Although we can talk about the equality of temperature intervals, we cannot meaningfully claim that a temperature of 20 °C is twice as hot as one of 10 °C, since the zero point on the Centigrade scale is not in any sense an absolute zero. For some variables, however – the *ratio variables* – there is an absolute zero, and ratios may validly be taken. Consider, for example, the time taken to utter a sentence. Someone who takes 2.48 seconds to utter the sentence takes exactly twice as long as someone who utters it in 1.24 seconds. Time is thus a ratio variable.

Most of the variables of interest in the natural and physical sciences are of the interval or ratio types, while many of those we encounter in the study of language are of the nominal or ordinal types. It is extremely important for investigators to know which type of variable they are dealing with, because different statistical procedures are appropriate for different types of variable, as we shall see in detail later. The level of measurement of the variable concerned influences the choice of a measure of typical value and variability, and also the choice of procedures for hypothesis testing. For interval or ratio variables, the so-called *parametric tests* can be used; but for nominal or ordinal variables, *non-parametric tests* are appropriate. We shall have more to say about this matter in chapter 6. Meanwhile, we should note that investigators of social and linguistic phenomena commonly assume a higher level of measurement than, strictly speaking, their data warrant.

Data which ought properly to be regarded as ordinal are often made to appear interval, by substituting numbers for ranks and then performing arithmetical operations on the numbers. The reason for this is that the parametric tests suitable for interval data are more powerful than non-parametric tests. As often happens in the application of statistical methods to real problems, practical considerations frequently outweigh the concerns of the theoretical purist.

## Exercises

1   Discuss alternative ways of selecting samples for each of the following investigations, commenting on the advantages and limitations of the methods you describe:

(i)   a comparison of word lengths in the plays of Shakespeare and Marlowe
(ii)   a study of some aspect of Cockney speech
(iii)   a study of syntactic complexity in the novels of Conrad

2   Classify each of the following as a nominal, ordinal, interval or ratio variable. Give reasons for your answers:

(i)   the length of pauses in a sample of conversation, measured in milliseconds
(ii)   the rating of words by informants, on a scale of pleasantness, ranging from 1 (very unpleasant) to 5 (very pleasant)
(iii)   the presence or absence of a finite verb in each clause in a particular text
(iv)   the degree of grammaticality of sentences, on a scale from 0 (absolutely ungrammatical) to 4 (entirely grammatical)
(v)   the number of sentences remembered correctly by informants ten minutes after first hearing them

# 2 Frequency distributions

## 2.1 The classification of raw data

As was mentioned in section 1.3, the raw data from an investigation usually require classification before patterns can readily be observed in them. Let us look again at the sets of scores obtained by the two groups of students in the hypothetical language teaching experiment discussed briefly in section 1.3, designed to test the effectiveness of the language laboratory as compared with more traditional methods. The data are repeated in table 2.1.

We notice that there seem to be more single-figure marks in the group B column than in the group A column, and that the range of marks for group B is larger than that for group A (5–18 as against 9–19). Otherwise, however, little pattern can be seen at a glance. Some of the scores in each column occur more than once. If we now count the frequency with which each score occurs in a given column, we obtain a *frequency distribution* for each set of scores, as shown in table 2.2. The picture is now clearer: we see that 15 is the most frequent score for group A, the frequencies falling away on either side of this score. The most frequent score for group B is 12, the frequencies again tailing away on either side. The frequency distributions also show clearly the difference in variability between the two sets of scores: the marks for group B are more spread than those for group A. Thus the frequency distribution will give us a rough idea about the *central tendency* of the scores and about their *variability*. Precise measures of these properties will be discussed in chapter 3.

## 2.2 Grouped data

A distribution giving a frequency for each individual value taken by the variable, as above, works well where there is a small number

**Table 2.1    Scores in a language test for two groups taught by different methods**

| *Marks out of 20* | |
|---|---|
| *Group A (Language laboratory) (N = 30)* | *Group B (Traditional) (N = 30)* |
| 15 | 11 |
| 12 | 16 |
| 11 | 14 |
| 18 | 18 |
| 15 | 6 |
| 15 | 8 |
| 9 | 9 |
| 19 | 14 |
| 14 | 12 |
| 13 | 12 |
| 11 | 10 |
| 12 | 15 |
| 18 | 12 |
| 15 | 9 |
| 16 | 13 |
| 14 | 16 |
| 16 | 17 |
| 17 | 12 |
| 15 | 8 |
| 17 | 7 |
| 13 | 15 |
| 14 | 5 |
| 13 | 14 |
| 15 | 13 |
| 17 | 13 |
| 19 | 12 |
| 17 | 11 |
| 18 | 13 |
| 16 | 11 |
| 14 | 7 |

of values (for instance, there are only 15 actual values of the variable in the language test data). Let us now consider what happens if the variable can take a wider range of values. The data in table 2.3 represent the frequency of sentences of particular lengths (in numbers of words) in the first 100 sentences of Iris Murdoch's *The Bell* (Penguin edition, 1962).

**Table 2.2    Frequency distributions for scores on language test**

| Score | Group A | | Group B | |
|---|---|---|---|---|
| 5 | | | / | 1 |
| 6 | | | / | 1 |
| 7 | | | // | 2 |
| 8 | | | // | 2 |
| 9 | / | 1 | // | 2 |
| 10 | | | / | 1 |
| 11 | // | 2 | /// | 3 |
| 12 | // | 2 | ///// | 5 |
| 13 | /// | 3 | //// | 4 |
| 14 | //// | 4 | /// | 3 |
| 15 | ///// / | 6 | // | 2 |
| 16 | /// | 3 | // | 2 |
| 17 | //// | 4 | / | 1 |
| 18 | /// | 3 | / | 1 |
| 19 | // | 2 | | |

Such a distribution is not, by itself, particularly useful, because there are large numbers of values taken by the variable (sentence length), many with very low frequencies. A clearer picture emerges if the sentence length values are grouped in the manner shown in table 2.4. Here, the data have been reclassified so that the total frequencies within the *class intervals* 1–5, 6–10, 11–15 and so on are recorded. Although we obtain a clearer idea of the distribution by grouping in this way, we also lose some of the original information. We know how many sentences have lengths in the range 1–5 words, but we no longer know, from the grouped data, what proportion of these have lengths of 1, 2, 3, 4 and 5 words. For the purpose of later statistical calculations, one of two assumptions can be made: either that the frequencies are evenly spread over the class interval (for example, 3.6 sentences of each of the lengths 6, 7, 8, 9 and 10 for the Iris Murdoch data); or that the total frequency within the class interval is concentrated at its mid-point (3, 8, 13, and so on, for the sentence length data). Which assumption we make depends on just what we want to do with the data, as we shall see later.

Table 2.3    Sentence length (words) distribution for the first 100
sentences of Iris Murdoch's *The Bell* (with hyphenated items
treated as single words)

| Sentence length (no. words) | Frequency | Sentence length (no. words) | Frequency |
|:---:|:---:|:---:|:---:|
| 3 | 1 | 23 | 4 |
| 4 |   | 24 | 2 |
| 5 | 1 | 25 | 4 |
| 6 | 2 | 26 |   |
| 7 | 2 | 27 | 1 |
| 8 | 8 | 28 | 3 |
| 9 | 3 | 29 | 3 |
| 10 | 3 | 30 | 2 |
| 11 | 5 | 31 | 1 |
| 12 | 3 | 32 | 2 |
| 13 | 3 | 33 | 2 |
| 14 | 8 | 34 | 1 |
| 15 | 7 | 35 |   |
| 16 | 3 | 36 | 2 |
| 17 | 4 | 37 | 1 |
| 18 | 1 | 38 | 1 |
| 19 | 6 | 39 |   |
| 20 | 4 | 40 | 1 |
| 21 | 2 | 41 |   |
| 22 | 3 | 42 | 1 |

Table 2.4    Grouped data for sentence length distribution

| Sentence length (no. words) | Frequency |
|:---:|:---:|
| 1- 5 | 2 |
| 6-10 | 18 |
| 11-15 | 26 |
| 16-20 | 18 |
| 21-25 | 15 |
| 26-30 | 9 |
| 31-35 | 6 |
| 36-40 | 5 |
| 41-45 | 1 |

## 2.3    Histograms

An even clearer idea of a frequency distribution can be obtained by converting it to a *histogram*. For data which are not grouped, we simply arrange the values taken by the variable on the horizontal axis, and frequency values on the vertical axis, and then draw a box or bar over each value taken by the variable, at a height corresponding to the frequency found for that value. The data for our hypothetical language teaching experiment are presented as histograms in figures 2.1 and 2.2.

If we are dealing with grouped data, the width of a box in the histogram corresponds to the class interval, as in figure 2.3 which shows the sentence length distribution of the data from *The Bell*. The horizontal axis is labelled with the mid-points of the class intervals.

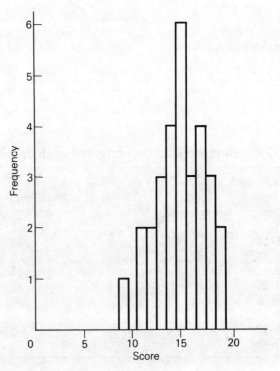

**Figure 2.1    Language test scores: group A**

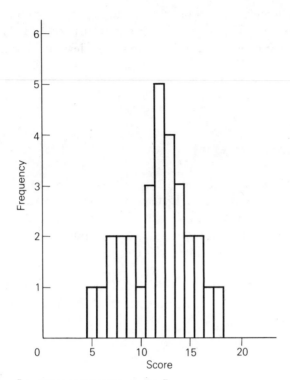

**Figure 2.2   Language test scores: group B**

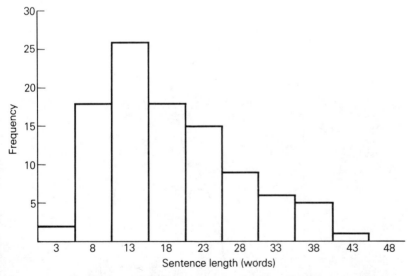

**Figure 2.3   Sentence length distribution for the first 100 sentences of Murdoch's *The Bell***

It is extremely important that histograms and other graphical representations of frequency distributions should be clearly labelled: they should have a title, and the relevant variables should be specified along each axis, together with the unit of measurement where appropriate.

## 2.4   Frequency polygons

An alternative way of presenting distributions graphically is to draw a *frequency polygon*. Instead of a box, we draw a point over the value of a variable at a height corresponding to the frequency of that value. If the data are grouped, the point is placed over the mid-point of the class interval. The points are then joined by straight lines, as shown in figures 2.4–2.7. Note that the graph is normally taken to zero at the limits of the range of values, where it is sensible to do so. One advantage of frequency polygons is

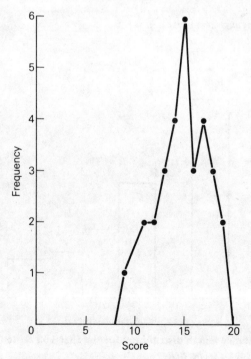

**Figure 2.4   Language test scores: group A**

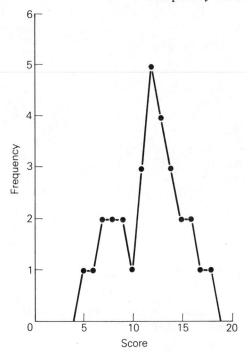

**Figure 2.5**    Language test scores: group B

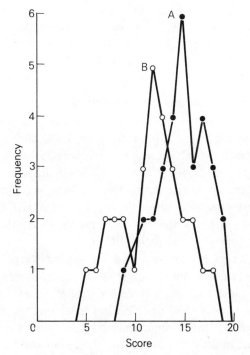

**Figure 2.6**    Language test scores: groups A and B

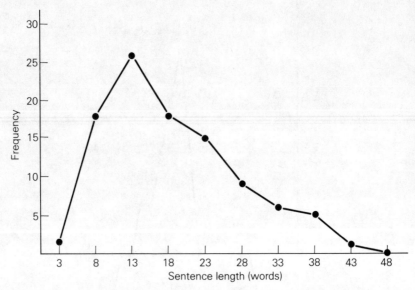

**Figure 2.7**   **Sentence length distribution for the first 100 sentences of Murdoch's** *The Bell*

that they provide an excellent visual means of comparing two distributions, by plotting them on the same graph. This is illustrated by figure 2.6 in which the distributions for the two groups of language learners are superimposed.

## 2.5   The shapes of frequency distributions

Because they are made up of straight lines, and represent data from a relatively small number of observations, the frequency polygons in figures 2.4–2.7 are irregular. If, however, we were to draw polygons for much larger sets of data, we should find that the irregularities would smooth out, so that we could draw a smooth curve through the points. The shape of the curve is an important property of the distribution.

A particularly important kind of distribution, the so-called *normal distribution*, has a bell-shaped curve, symmetrical about its highest point, as shown in figure 2.8. We shall investigate the properties of the normal distribution in chapter 4. Meanwhile, it does not take too much imagination to see that the distributions given by our language test results approximate to the 'normal' shape. If a distribution is lopsided rather than symmetrical, it is said to be *skewed*. If the high frequencies correspond to low values of the variable, as in the sentence length distribution in figures 2.3 and 2.7, the distribution is *positively skewed*; if the higher frequencies are at higher values, it is *negatively skewed* (see figure 2.9).

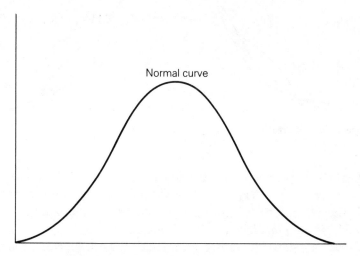

**Figure 2.8    Normal distribution curve**

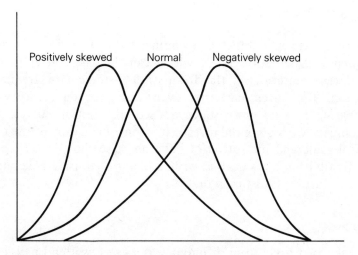

**Figure 2.9    Skewed distributions**

**Figure 2.10    Kurtosis**

A further property of distribution curves is their *kurtosis*. This refers to the degree of peaking: if a curve is more peaked than the normal distribution, it is said to be *leptokurtic*; if less peaked, it is *platykurtic* (see figure 2.10). Kurtosis is not as important as skewedness in later statistical work on a distribution, and we shall not discuss it further here.

## 2.6   Conclusion

The first stage in a statistical examination of data is to prepare a frequency distribution table, which can then be converted to a visual representation in the form of a histogram or frequency polygon. The latter have the advantage of greater clarity when comparing two or more superimposed distribution curves. This preliminary work gives the investigator some indication of the most typical value and the spread of data, and also shows the shape of the distribution he is dealing with, a factor of considerable importance in further statistical work.

### Exercises

1   Take two texts from different varieties of written English and draw up a frequency distribution for the lengths of the first 200

words in each text, making clear your criteria for defining a word. Plot your distributions (i) as histograms, (ii) as frequency polygons. Comment on the shapes of the distributions, and on any differences you observe.

2   In a study by Crompton, the intensity of stressed and unstressed syllables (in decibels from an arbitrary norm) was measured in a sample of spoken French. The results for the first 100 syllables of each type were as follows:

*Stressed*

| | | | | | | | | | |
|---|---|---|---|---|---|---|---|---|---|
| 21 | 30 | 28 | 19 | 21 | 19 | 20 | 22 | 26 | 22 |
| 26 | 23 | 21 | 30 | 25 | 27 | 26 | 25 | 31 | 26 |
| 27 | 22 | 16 | 18 | 29 | 23 | 19 | 24 | 24 | 25 |
| 25 | 25 | 25 | 19 | 24 | 20 | 24 | 20 | 20 | 25 |
| 22 | 20 | 22 | 22 | 22 | 26 | 27 | 22 | 25 | 30 |
| 27 | 20 | 25 | 24 | 22 | 21 | 28 | 24 | 23 | 23 |
| 26 | 29 | 31 | 23 | 29 | 27 | 28 | 31 | 29 | 27 |
| 16 | 19 | 23 | 23 | 19 | 25 | 23 | 28 | 26 | 25 |
| 26 | 23 | 31 | 23 | 31 | 27 | 29 | 25 | 30 | 27 |
| 27 | 22 | 25 | 21 | 24 | 25 | 20 | 22 | 21 | 28 |

*Unstressed*

| | | | | | | | | | |
|---|---|---|---|---|---|---|---|---|---|
| 25 | 29 | 27 | 23 | 18 | 22 | 24 | 21 | 25 | 14 |
| 25 | 22 | 25 | 29 | 25 | 19 | 26 | 25 | 28 | 20 |
| 23 | 25 | 22 | 27 | 27 | 21 | 22 | 22 | 27 | 23 |
| 21 | 28 | 24 | 21 | 26 | 24 | 18 | 23 | 22 | 25 |
| 22 | 24 | 21 | 21 | 22 | 16 | 25 | 16 | 23 | 22 |
| 28 | 20 | 15 | 28 | 25 | 15 | 10 | 14 | 19 | 24 |
| 25 | 20 | 22 | 20 | 23 | 22 | 7 | 20 | 26 | 21 |
| 28 | 25 | 23 | 23 | 14 | 28 | 20 | 22 | 28 | 21 |
| 30 | 28 | 20 | 16 | 18 | 29 | 16 | 25 | 24 | 16 |
| 25 | 28 | 20 | 19 | 21 | 24 | 26 | 25 | 28 | 14 |

Group the data using an appropriate interval, and draw frequency polygons to compare the distribution of intensities for stressed and unstressed syllables. Comment on the results.

3   In the same study of French, the length of pause (in units of 1/50 sec) was measured for each tone group boundary which was not sentence-final. The results were as follows:

| 33 | 22 | 28 | 33 | 16 | 2  | 26 | 7  | 22 | 9  |
|----|----|----|----|----|----|----|----|----|----|
| 18 | 26 | 7  | 22 | 25 | 5  | 2  | 13 | 6  | 11 |
| 5  | 26 | 22 | 30 | 32 | 37 | 14 | 5  | 33 | 36 |
| 24 | 35 | 31 | 34 | 10 | 27 | 10 | 5  | 8  | 11 |
| 6  | 7  | 17 | 31 | 9  | 8  | 19 | 0  | 6  | 22 |
| 33 | 3  | 21 | 2  | 27 | 27 | 24 | 0  | 10 | 34 |
| 3  | 37 | 21 | 9  | 19 | 4  | 12 | 17 | 24 | 11 |
| 6  | 4  | 15 | 3  | 33 | 21 | 34 | 40 | 7  | 0  |
| 3  | 29 | 25 | 25 | 3  | 33 | 10 | 41 | 13 | 0  |
| 28 | 19 | 14 | 2  | 0  | 2  | 25 | 22 | 22 | 0  |
| 26 | 4  | 25 | 25 | 0  | 0  | 24 | 20 | 25 | 0  |
| 7  | 22 | 21 | 10 | 30 | 30 | 10 | 22 | 9  | 0  |
| 0  | 3  | 16 | 28 | 5  | 6  | 28 | 23 | 10 | 18 |
| 22 | 30 | 34 | 25 | 23 | 30 | 28 | 25 | 1  | 16 |
| 7  | 4  | 17 | 5  | 28 | 13 | 25 | 23 | 13 | 0  |

Group these data using an appropriate interval, and draw a histogram of the grouped frequency distribution. Comment on the results.

# 3 Measures of central tendency and variability

## 3.1 Introduction

In chapter 2, we saw that a table setting out the frequency distribution of a set of data and, even better, a histogram or frequency polygon, gave some idea of two important properties of the distribution: the value or range of values around which the data typically cluster, and the extent of variability in the data. In the present chapter, we shall discuss precise quantitative measures of these properties.

## 3.2 Measures of central tendency

Three measures of central tendency are available: the *mean*, the *median* and the *mode*. We shall first define these and show how they may be calculated; we shall then discuss the factors involved in deciding which is the appropriate measure to use in any given case.

### 3.2.1 The mean

The 'mean' is what the layman means by an 'average', although the statistician would regard all three measures of central tendency as types of average. To obtain the mean of a set of figures, we add up all the figures and divide by the total number of observations. Since we shall need to use algebraic notation for the rather more complex formulae to be introduced later, let us break ourselves in gently by developing a very simple expression for the mean. If we let $x$ stand for any of the numbers whose mean we are trying to compute, then $\Sigma x$ (read as 'sigma x', $\Sigma$ being a Greek capital sigma) is the sum of all the $x$'s, that is the sum of all our numbers. If the total number of observations is $N$, then

$$\text{mean} = \frac{\Sigma x}{N} = \bar{x} \quad \text{(read as 'x-bar')}.$$

Let us now use this formula to calculate the mean score for group A in the language teaching experiment discussed in chapter 2 (for data see table 2.1).

$$
\begin{aligned}
\text{mean} = \frac{\Sigma x}{N} = (&15 + 12 + 11 + 18 + 15 + 15 + 9 + 19 \\
&+ 14 + 13 + 11 + 12 + 18 + 15 + 16 + 14 \\
&+ 16 + 17 + 15 + 17 + 13 + 14 + 13 + 15 \\
&+ 17 + 19 + 17 + 18 + 16 + 14)/30 \\
&= 448/30 = 14.93.
\end{aligned}
$$

The mean can be calculated rather more conveniently from a frequency distribution table. If we now let $x$ stand for any particular value of the variable, and $f$ for the frequency with which that value appears in the data, then

$$\text{mean} = \frac{\Sigma f x}{N}.$$

This means that we take each value, multiply by its frequency in the data, add the results, and then divide by $N$. This is done below for the data from group A of the language teaching experiment (see table 2.2):

$$
\begin{aligned}
\text{mean} = \frac{\Sigma f x}{N} = \{&(1 \times 9) + (2 \times 11) + (2 \times 12) + (3 \times 13) \\
&+ (4 \times 14) + (6 \times 15) + (3 \times 16) + (4 \times 17) \\
&+ (3 \times 18) + (2 \times 19)\}/30 \\
&= 448/30 = 14.93.
\end{aligned}
$$

We may also wish to calculate a mean from a grouped frequency distribution, such as that in table 3.1, which relates to a study in

Table 3.1    Times taken to utter a sentence

| Time (sec) | Frequency |
|------------|-----------|
| 3.1–3.5 | 5 |
| 3.6–4.0 | 18 |
| 4.1–4.5 | 25 |
| 4.6–5.0 | 27 |
| 5.1–5.5 | 20 |
| 5.6–6.0 | 5 |

Table 3.2    Steps in the calculation of the mean utterance time

| Time (sec) | Mid-point of interval | Frequency | Frequency × mid-point value |
|------------|-----------------------|-----------|------------------------------|
| 3.1–3.5 | 3.3 | 5 | 16.5 |
| 3.6–4.0 | 3.8 | 18 | 68.4 |
| 4.1–4.5 | 4.3 | 25 | 107.5 |
| 4.6–5.0 | 4.8 | 27 | 129.6 |
| 5.1–5.5 | 5.3 | 20 | 106.0 |
| 5.6–6.0 | 5.8 | 5 | 29.0 |
|  |  | 100 | 457.0 |

$$\bar{x} = \frac{457.0}{100} = 4.57 \text{ sec}$$

which the times taken to utter a particular sentence have been measured for 100 speakers. To calculate the mean, we regard the total frequency within each class interval as being concentrated at the mid-point of that interval. We then calculate, for each interval, the product of frequency and mid-point value, sum over all the intervals, and finally divide by the total number of observations. These steps are summarised in table 3.2.

### 3.2.2    The median

Let us suppose that we have arranged a set of figures in order from highest to lowest, that is, in 'rank' order. The median value is that value which has equal numbers of observations above it and below it. If the distribution is represented graphically, a vertical dropped at the median value cuts the area of the graph in half.

We shall now consider the calculation of the median for a small set of figures. The number of words in each line of Sylvia Plath's 19-line poem 'Strumpet Song' (from *The Colossus*, Faber paperback edition, 1972) is given below (a word being any stretch of language between two spaces):

4, 7, 5, 7, 7, 3, 4, 4, 5, 5, 3, 5, 5, 7, 4, 9, 8, 6, 2.

Arranging these figures in ascending order, we have

2, 3, 3, 4, 4, 4, 4, 5, 5, 5, 5, 5, 6, 7, 7, 7, 7, 8, 9.

The middle value in a set of 19 is the tenth, which in the present case is 5. There are seven lines with a length lower than 5, and seven with a length higher than 5. The median line length for the poem is thus 5 words.

In the above case, it was easy to find the median, because there was just one value with equal numbers of observations above and below it. This is not always so, however, as can be seen by considering the data from class B in our language teaching experiment (see table 2.1). For one thing, there is an even number of observations ($N = 30$), so that there cannot be one that is right in the middle. In such a case, we take the mean of the two central figures (here, the fifteenth and sixteenth). The values are most readily obtained from a frequency distribution table (table 2.2). If we start at the lowest value of the variable, and begin to add up frequencies, we find that 12 observations lie in the range up to and including 11 marks, and since there are five scores of 12, the fifteenth and sixteenth scores must both be 12. We might therefore say that the median value is a score of 12. A moment's thought, however, will show that this is only an approximate value for the median. There are 12 scores below 12 in the table, but 13 above 12. Since the median is defined as that score having exactly equal numbers of observations above and below it, we have clearly achieved only an approximate solution.

We can, however, compute a more accurate value if required. If we give any figure to the nearest whole number, then any whole number can represent a more exact figure up to 0.5 below or above it. For example, any number between 11.50 and 12.49 (assuming we are working to two decimal places) will become 12 when expressed to the nearest whole number. If we now regard the score 12 as representing a range of values from 11.50 up to 12.49, and if we also assume that each of the scores of 12 in our table takes up an equal part of this interval, then each of the five will represent 0.2 of a point – 11.50 up to but not including 11.70, 11.70 up to 11.90, 11.90 up to 12.10, 12.10 up to 12.30 and 12.30 up to 12.50. The fifteenth score is thus taken to represent the range 11.90 up to 12.10, and the sixteenth, the range from 12.10 up to 12.30. From this, it is clear that the median is 12.10. The procedure we have just followed may be expressed as a general formula:

$$\text{median} = L + \left(\frac{N/2 - F}{f_m}\right)h$$

where

$L$ = lower limit of interval containing the median
$F$ = sum of all frequencies below the limit $L$
$f_m$ = frequency within the interval containing the median
$N$ = number of observations
$h$ = width of class interval (for grouped data).

For the class B scores, we have

$L$ = 11.50
$F$ = 12
$f_m$ = 5
$N$ = 30
$h$ = 1 (since the data are ungrouped, so that the 'class interval' is just 1 mark)

so that

$$\text{median} = 11.50 + \left(\frac{30/2 - 12}{5}\right) \times 1 = 11.50 + 0.6 = 12.10.$$

Fortunately, it is not often necessary to express the median to this degree of accuracy.

### 3.2.3  The mode

The mode is simply that value which has the highest frequency. It is most readily obtained from a frequency distribution table or graphical representation. For group A in the language teaching experiment the modal value is 15; for group B it is 12. Sometimes it is not possible to compute a mode for a set of data. Consider, for example, the figures 1, 1, 1, 2, 2, 2, 3, 3, 3. Here, each value occurs three times, so there is no one value with a frequency higher than the others. In other cases, the distribution may have two or more peaks: one with two maxima is said to be *bimodal*.

### 3.2.4  Choosing a measure of central tendency

The choice of an appropriate measure of central tendency depends on three considerations:

1    the level of measurement of the variable concerned (nominal, ordinal, interval or ratio – see section 1.4);
2    the shape of the frequency distribution (see section 2.5);
3    what is to be done with the figure obtained.

The mean is really suitable only for ratio and interval data. For ordinal variables, where the data can be ranked but one cannot validly talk of 'equal differences' between values, the median, which is based on ranking, may be used. Where it is not even possible to rank the data, as in the case of a nominal variable, the mode may be the only measure available.

Given that we have, say, an interval variable, for which any of the three measures would be valid on the above grounds, the other factors mentioned earlier come into play. It should be remembered that the point of measures of central tendency is to give a 'typical' value around which the data cluster. Let us imagine that we have measured the number of words in each chapter of a novel, and obtained the following results: 4 841, 4 724, 3 420, 3 861, 4 017, 5 129, 3 450, 3 481, 5 001, 4 482, 17 807. Clearly, the last figure is highly untypical of the general run. If we were to calculate the mean, this untypical figure would count just as much as any of the others, since the mean takes account of the absolute size of each observation (the mean, to the nearest whole number, is in fact 5 474 words, which is above the highest of the more typical values). The median, however, takes account only of the position of each value in a ranking hierarchy. Thus it would not matter, for the purpose of calculating the median, if the last figure were 5 200, 8 000 or even 100 000: only its position as the highest value would be reflected. The median is therefore useful when a distribution contains one or more highly untypical values. Of course, these untypical values may be extremely significant from the point of view of interpretation (*why* is the last chapter between three and four times longer than the others?), but they should not be allowed to distort the measure of central tendency.

Another way of putting this is that, if the distribution is strongly skewed, either positively or negatively, the median is a better indicator of central tendency than the mean. In order to investigate the relationship between mean, median and mode for a skewed distribution, we shall calculate these statistics for the sentence length distribution data discussed in section 2.2 (see table 2.3). From the data in the table, we calculate the mean as

$$\bar{x} = \frac{\Sigma fx}{N} = \frac{1\,860}{100} = 18.60 \text{ words.}$$

For the median, we need to find a value below and above which there are 100/2 or 50 observations. There are 49 observations of 16 words or below, and 51 of 17 or above, so that the median clearly lies in the region 16–17 words. The more exact method of calculation gives the following results:

$$\text{median} = L + \left(\frac{N/2 - F}{f_m}\right) h = 16.5 + \left(\frac{100/2 - 49}{4}\right) \times 1$$

$$= 16.75 \text{ words.}$$

The distribution is slightly bimodal, having frequencies of 8 for the values 8 and 14 words; grouping of the data as in table 2.4 shows that the mode lies in the interval 11–15 words when calculated according to this grouping. Thus we see that, for a positively skewed distribution, the three measures of central tendency differ, the mean being higher than the median, which is in turn higher than the mode. This is illustrated in figure 3.1. The relationships would be in the reverse direction for a negatively skewed distribution.

For a symmetrical distribution, the mean, median and mode are very close: indeed, where the distribution is completely sym-

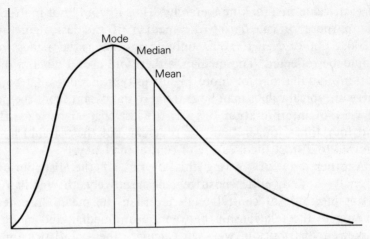

**Figure 3.1** **Mean, median and mode for a positively skewed distribution**

metrical, as in the normal curve, the three coincide. The following are the values of the three measures for our language test data:

*Group A:* mean score = 14.93;
median score = 15.00;
modal score = 15
*Group B:* mean score = 11.77;
median score = 12.10;
modal score = 12

In such cases, the mean is the most representative statistic, since, as we have seen, it takes account not only of the ranking of the data, but also of their absolute values. The mean has a further advantage: it has properties which make it particularly suitable for further statistical procedures, which we shall consider later.

Where it is appropriate, then, the mean should be used in preference to (or in addition to) the median and/or mode. But we should remember that many of the variables in which the linguist is interested are ordinal, so that the median may often be the most appropriate measure.

### 3.3  Measures of variability

#### 3.3.1  Why study variability?

We now turn to the question of variability: how closely do the data cluster round the most typical value? Before considering measures of variability in some detail, we should consider why we bother to measure this property at all. Variability may be of interest in its own right; it may be more important, when attempting to obtain, say, a stylistic profile of an author's works, to determine whether he uses a wide range of sentence lengths or a narrow range, than to calculate a most typical value for sentence length. Variability is also important when we are trying to compare two sets of data. In our language teaching experiment, for example, we are interested in determining whether the mean scores for the two groups are really significantly different. We can claim a difference in means much more confidently if the values for each set cluster closely round the central value than if they are widely spread. Indeed, certain valuable tests of differences between means assume that the sets of data show roughly equal variability. We shall go into these matters in more detail in chapters 6 and 7.

### 3.3.2   A simple measure of variability: the range

The simplest indicator of variability in a set of data is the range, that is, the difference between the highest and lowest values. But although the range can be useful as a crude measure, it can also be misleading. Consider again the study of chapter lengths in a novel, discussed in section 3.2.4. The data were: 4 841, 4 724, 3 420, 3 861, 4 017, 5 129, 3 450, 3 481, 5 001, 4 482 and 17 807 words. The range here is (17 807 − 3 420) or 14 387 words. But this is high because of just one value (the 'untypical' highest value), and gives no indication of the rather small variability in the rest of the novel. Nevertheless, where the distribution is fairly symmetrical, it may be worth calculating the range as a first step in the examination of variability. The following sets of figures demonstrate that the range can vary widely even when the mean is kept constant:

1, 4, 9, 11, 15, 19, 24, 29, 34      Mean 16.22   Range 33
14, 15, 15, 16, 16, 16, 18, 18, 18      Mean 16.22   Range  4

### 3.3.3   The interquartile range and quartile deviation

Just as the median is that value above and below which half the data in a distribution lie, so we may define *quartiles*, which cut the distribution into quarters. The first quartile (sometimes called the twenty-fifth percentile) is the value below which one-quarter of the observations lie; the median is really the second quartile; the third quartile is the value below which three-quarters of the observations lie. The difference between the first and third quartiles is known as the *interquartile range*, and half this value is the *quartile deviation*. These measures are useful for skewed distributions, since, like the median, they are insensitive to odd extreme values. Thus, in cases where the median is an appropriate measure of central tendency, the interquartile range or quartile deviation is often a suitable measure of variability.

Let us now calculate the interquartile range and quartile deviation for the sentence length data in table 2.3: 25 of the 100 values lie below 12 (or, more precisely, below the limit of 11.50); 75 observations lie below 25 (that is, the limit of 24.50). The interquartile range is thus $25 - 12$ (or $24.50 - 11.50$), or 13 words, and the quartile deviation is 13/2 or 6.50 words.

An exactly parallel procedure lies behind the calculation of *deciles*, values which cut the distribution into ten parts, and *percentiles*, which divide it into 100 parts.

### 3.3.4  The mean deviation

A rather more sophisticated measure of variability than the range is the mean deviation, which takes all the values into account. To calculate the mean deviation, we subtract the mean from each observation, ignore the sign of the result and add all the deviations together, then divide by the number of observations:

$$\text{mean deviation} = \frac{\Sigma \, |x - \bar{x}|}{N}$$

where

$\Sigma$ means 'sum of', as usual
$x$ is any value
$\bar{x}$ is the mean value
$N$ is the total number of observations
$|\ \ |$ means 'take the absolute value, ignoring the sign'.

The mean deviation is a common-sense measure with a readily interpretable meaning: it is the average deviation of the values from the mean, irrespective of which side of the mean they are on. Unfortunately, it is mathematically unsuitable for more advanced statistical work, and so is hardly ever used.

### 3.3.5    The variance and standard deviation

Unlike the mean deviation, the so-called *standard deviation*, though difficult to interpret in common-sense terms, has properties which make it very suitable for further statistical work. It is therefore the most widely used measure of variability for variables with an interval or ratio level of measurement. As we shall see below, the standard deviation is closely related to a further measure of variability, the *variance*.

To calculate the standard deviation, we first find the deviation of each observation from the mean. This, it will be remembered, was also the first step in the calculation of the mean deviation. Some of the differences will be positive, others negative. We can get rid of the sign difference, not this time by simply taking absolute values, but by squaring the values, thereby always obtaining a positive number. We then add the squared values to obtain the 'sum of squares'. Dividing by the number of observations gives us the variance, and the square root of this is the standard deviation. This can be expressed algebraically as follows:

$$\text{variance} = \frac{\Sigma(x - \bar{x})^2}{N}$$

$$\text{standard deviation} = \sqrt{\text{variance}} = \sqrt{\frac{\Sigma(x - \bar{x})^2}{N}}.$$

There is one slight complication in this otherwise fairly simple story, concerned with the difference between population parameters and sample statistics (see section 1.2). The standard deviation of a variable in a population is given the symbol $\sigma$, and the variance is thus $\sigma^2$ (remember that Greek letters are used for population parameters). Often, however, we do not know the characteristics of the whole population, but only of a sample. In this case, we have a statistic, symbolised as $s$, which is an estimate of the population parameter $\sigma$, the variance of the sample being $s^2$. It can be shown that, when we are estimating the standard deviation, we obtain a biased estimate if we divide by $N$ as in the above formulae. If, however, we divide by $(N-1)$ instead, we obtain an unbiased estimate. It is therefore safest to use the following formulae when calculating the variance and standard deviation of a sample:

$$\text{variance} \quad = s^2 = \frac{\Sigma(x-\bar{x})^2}{N-1}$$

$$\text{standard deviation} = s = \sqrt{\frac{\Sigma(x-\bar{x})^2}{N-1}} \; .$$

Where the number of observations, $N$, is large, the results given by the formula with $N$ and those with $(N-1)$ are very close.

The above form of the standard deviation formula is often rather inconvenient computationally, since the mean will usually be a number expressed to a certain number of decimal places, and its subtraction from each observation not only is tedious, but also introduces errors arising from the original rounding of the mean to the number of decimal places used. It is quite easy to show that the formula can be rewritten in a form that does not involve the mean. We can expand the bracketed expression in the top line of the formula as follows:

$$\Sigma(x-\bar{x})^2 = \Sigma(x^2 - 2x\bar{x} + \bar{x}^2).$$

Since $\Sigma$ simply means 'sum of', we can apply it separately to each part of this expression, giving

$$\Sigma x^2 - \Sigma 2x\bar{x} + \Sigma \bar{x}^2.$$

But since $2\bar{x}$ (twice the mean) is constant for a given set of data, we can take it outside the summation sign in the second term of the expression. Furthermore, the last term means 'add the mean squared, for each observation'. Since there are $N$ observations in all, this last term is equivalent to $N\bar{x}^2$. We therefore now have:

$$\Sigma x^2 - 2\bar{x}\Sigma x + N\bar{x}^2.$$

We can now eliminate $\bar{x}$ by using the relationship

$$\bar{x} = \frac{\Sigma x}{N} \; .$$

Substituting this in the expression above, we now have

$$\Sigma x^2 - 2\frac{\Sigma x}{N}\cdot\Sigma x + N\left(\frac{\Sigma x}{N}\right)^2 = \Sigma x^2 - \frac{2(\Sigma x)^2}{N} + \frac{N(\Sigma x)^2}{N^2}$$

$$= \Sigma x^2 - \frac{2(\Sigma x)^2}{N} + \frac{(\Sigma x)^2}{N}$$

$$= \Sigma x^2 - \frac{(\Sigma x)^2}{N}$$

This, then, is the top line for our new expression for the standard deviation, which is

$$s = \sqrt{\frac{\Sigma x^2 - (\Sigma x)^2/N}{N-1}}.$$

Readers should not worry unduly if they find the above manipulations quite difficult: they are presented here only because it can be frustrating to many people to be given a formula without any explanation of its origin. What is important is that we should understand exactly what the new formula means. We first square each observation and sum the squares. We also need to find the sum of the observations, square it, and divide by $N$. We now take this figure from the sum of squares, and divide the result by $(N-1)$ to give the variance. The standard deviation is the square root of the variance, as usual.

We can facilitate the calculation of the standard deviation still further by taking our data from a frequency distribution table. Instead of '$x$' (any particular observed value) we now have '$fx$' in our formula: each possible value, multiplied by the frequency of that value in the data. We thus write

$$s = \sqrt{\frac{\Sigma fx^2 - (\Sigma fx)^2/N}{N-1}}.$$

It is very important to note the difference, in this expression, between $\Sigma fx^2$, which means 'square each possible value of $x$ and multiply by the frequency with which that value occurs in the data; then add up all the resulting figures', and $(\Sigma fx)^2$, which means 'multiply each possible value of $x$ by its frequency in the data, add up all the resulting figures, then take the square of this sum.'

Table 3.3    Scores on language tests for groups A and B

| | Frequencies | |
|---|---|---|
| Score | Group A | Group B |
| 5 | | 1 |
| 6 | | 1 |
| 7 | | 2 |
| 8 | | 2 |
| 9 | 1 | 2 |
| 10 | | 1 |
| 11 | 2 | 3 |
| 12 | 2 | 5 |
| 13 | 3 | 4 |
| 14 | 4 | 3 |
| 15 | 6 | 2 |
| 16 | 3 | 2 |
| 17 | 4 | 1 |
| 18 | 3 | 1 |
| 19 | 2 | |

Let us now calculate the standard deviations of the two sets of scores obtained in our language teaching experiment. The data from table 2.2 are repeated for convenience in table 3.3.

For group A:

$$\Sigma fx^2 = (1 \times 9^2) + (2 \times 11^2) + (2 \times 12^2) + (3 \times 13^2)$$
$$+ (4 \times 14^2) + (6 \times 15^2) + (3 \times 16^2) + (4 \times 17^2)$$
$$+ (3 \times 18^2) + (2 \times 19^2)$$
$$= 6\,870.$$

$$\Sigma fx = (1 \times 9) + (2 \times 11) + (2 \times 12) + (3 \times 13) + (4 \times 14)$$
$$+ (6 \times 15) + (3 \times 16) + (4 \times 17) + (3 \times 18) + (2 \times 19)$$
$$= 448.$$

$$s^2 = \frac{\Sigma fx^2 - (\Sigma fx)^2/N}{N-1} = \frac{6\,870 - 448^2/30}{30-1} = \frac{6\,870 - 6\,690.13}{29}$$

$$= 6.20.$$

$$s = \sqrt{6.20} = 2.49 \text{ marks.}$$

For group B:

$$\Sigma fx^2 = (1 \times 5^2) + (1 \times 6^2) + (2 \times 7^2) + (2 \times 8^2) + (2 \times 9^2)$$
$$+ (1 \times 10^2) + (3 \times 11^2) + (5 \times 12^2) + (4 \times 13^2)$$
$$+ (3 \times 14^2) + (2 \times 15^2) + (2 \times 16^2) + (1 \times 17^2)$$
$$+ (1 \times 18^2)$$
$$= 4\,471.$$

$$\Sigma fx = (1 \times 5) + (1 \times 6) + (2 \times 7) + (2 \times 8) + (2 \times 9)$$
$$+ (1 \times 10) + (3 \times 11) + (5 \times 12) + (4 \times 13) + (3 \times 14)$$
$$+ (2 \times 15) + (2 \times 16) + (1 \times 17) + (1 \times 18)$$
$$= 353.$$

$$s^2 = \frac{4\,471 - 353^2/30}{30-1} = \frac{4\,471 - 4\,153.63}{29} = 10.94.$$

$$s = \sqrt{10.94} = 3.31 \text{ marks.}$$

We see that the data for group B show slightly more variability than those for group A.

Finally, we should mention one device that is sometimes useful in calculating the standard deviation. If we subtract a given quantity from each observed figure, the variance and standard deviation are unaltered. The subtraction of a constant in this way is useful if the figures are all high. For example, for the set of data 1 024, 1 010, 1 009, 1 074, 1 068, 1 006, 1 089, we could subtract 1 000 from each before going on to calculate the standard deviation, and the result will be just the same as if we had used the original figures. This makes sense if we remember that the standard deviation is calculated from the squares of *differences* between observed values and the mean. If we are operating with differences, rather than absolute values, the subtraction of a constant from each value will not affect the result, since the mean will also differ by this constant from the true mean.

## Exercises

1  (i)  In what ways can we measure
        (a) the most typical value

      (b) the spread, or variability, of values
in a set of data?

(ii)  What criteria govern the selection of particular measures of central tendency and variability?

(iii) Calculate appropriate measures of central tendency and variability for the following data, representing pause lengths in milliseconds:

24 13 16 17 20 22 29 14 15 24 19 20 19 18 18
22 21 21 23 25 14 17 20 21 20 22 23 26 21 18

2   From the data on word length collected for question 1 of the exercises to chapter 2, calculate the mean, median and mode for each sample. Which is the most appropriate measure of central tendency for these data?

3   From the data on intensity of stressed and unstressed syllables given in question 2 of the exercises to chapter 2, calculate the mean, median, mode, range and standard deviation for each sample. Comment on the results.

4   Suppose that the following scores were obtained on administering a language proficiency test to ten aphasics who had undergone a course of treatment, and ten otherwise similar aphasics who had not undergone the treatment:

| *Experimental group* | *Control group* |
|---|---|
| 15 | 31 |
| 28 | 34 |
| 62 | 47 |
| 17 | 41 |
| 31 | 28 |
| 58 | 54 |
| 45 | 36 |
| 11 | 38 |
| 76 | 45 |
| 43 | 32 |

Calculate the mean score and standard deviation for each group, and comment on the results.

5   In an investigation carried out by the author (see Butler, 1982), native speakers of English were played a tape recording of

sentences which could be used to get someone to open a
window (for instance, 'Open the window'; 'Could you open
the window?'). They were asked to grade each sentence for
politeness, on a scale from 1 (very impolite) to 7 (very polite),
given that the situation involved two acquaintances of the
same age, sex and status. For two of the sentences, 50 of the
informants gave the following ratings:

*Sentence 1*

| 1 | 3 | 2 | 1 | 2 | 1 | 2 | 1 | 4 | 3 | 1 | 1 | 2 | 1 | 1 |
|---|---|---|---|---|---|---|---|---|---|---|---|---|---|---|
| 1 | 2 | 5 | 1 | 2 | 1 | 1 | 2 | 2 | 1 | 1 | 2 | 2 | 2 | 1 |
| 2 | 3 | 1 | 1 | 2 | 2 | 3 | 1 | 3 | 3 | 1 | 1 | 2 | 1 | 2 |
| 1 | 7 | 2 | 4 | 1 | | | | | | | | | | |

*Sentence 2*

| 3 | 3 | 4 | 2 | 3 | 4 | 1 | 4 | 3 | 1 | 2 | 3 | 2 | 4 | 2 |
|---|---|---|---|---|---|---|---|---|---|---|---|---|---|---|
| 4 | 3 | 3 | 1 | 1 | 2 | 2 | 4 | 3 | 1 | 2 | 3 | 3 | 1 | 4 |
| 3 | 3 | 1 | 3 | 2 | 5 | 2 | 2 | 2 | 2 | 1 | 4 | 2 | 2 | 1 |
| 4 | 2 | 4 | 4 | 2 | | | | | | | | | | |

Decide on the most appropriate measure of central tendency,
and calculate a value for it for each set of data.

# 4 The normal distribution

## 4.1 The importance of the normal distribution

We saw in section 2.5 that, if we took a very large population (or indeed very large samples from a population) and drew a frequency polygon to represent the distribution, we should be able to construct a smooth curve through the points. We also mentioned that one particular kind of frequency distribution, the so-called 'normal' distribution, is of special importance in statistical work. There are several reasons for this. Firstly, many properties found in the natural world, and of interest to natural and social scientists, are distributed according to the normal curve. Secondly, the normal distribution has certain special mathematical properties which make it possible to predict what proportion of the population will have values of a normally distributed variable within a given range. Thirdly, some important tests for significant differences between sets of data assume that the variables concerned are normally distributed.

## 4.2 The properties of the normal curve

As we saw earlier, the normal curve is bell-shaped and symmetrical about its highest point, at which the mean, median and mode of the distribution all coincide, as shown in figure 4.1. Certain important properties of the curve are concerned with the way in which the area under it is cut up by lines drawn vertically from different points on the horizontal axis. In order to understand this, let us return for a moment to the histograms we discussed in section 2.3. The height of each box in a histogram is proportional to the frequency being represented. Since the width of each box is the same, the area of the box is also proportional to the frequency of observations in the interval (which may be one unit or more: see the discussion of grouped frequency distributions in section 2.2) represented by that box. Now, a curve such as the normal curve is simply the limiting, smoothed-out shape we should get if we took a large number of observations and made our class intervals (that is, the width of our histogram boxes) very small. This is shown diagrammatically in figure 4.2. It follows that the area under the curve between two vertical lines drawn at particular values on the horizontal axis is proportional to the frequency of observations occurring between these two values of the variable. This would be true for any frequency curve, not just for the normal curve. However, the normal curve has special additional properties, which we shall now discuss.

The normal curve is entirely defined by just two properties of the distribution: the mean and the standard deviation. If we know these two values, we can construct the whole curve, by means of a rather complicated formula which will not be discussed here. A particularly important point is that a vertical line drawn at any given (whole or fractional) number of standard deviations from the mean will cut off a 'tail' containing a constant proportion of the total area under the curve, which can be read off from a statistical table such as that given as table A2 of appendix 1. A line

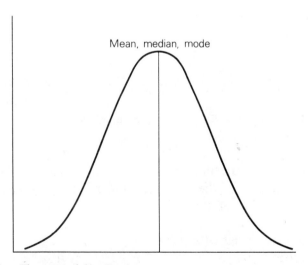

Mean, median, mode

**Figure 4.1**   **The normal distribution curve**

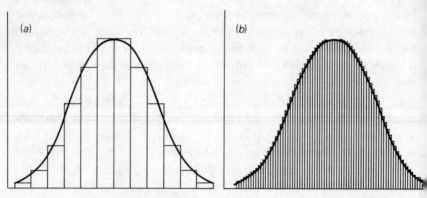

**Figure 4.2    Smoothing of the curve as interval width decreases: (a) wide intervals; (b) narrow intervals**

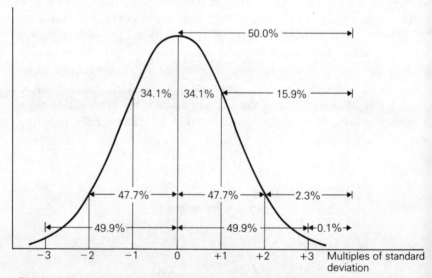

**Figure 4.3    Areas under the normal distribution curve**

drawn one standard deviation above the mean cuts off a tail containing 0.1587 of the total area under the curve; a line drawn at twice the value of the standard deviation cuts off 0.0228 of the area; and a line drawn three standard deviations above the mean produces a tail with just 0.0013 of the area. Since the curve is symmetrical, the same is true for lines drawn below the mean. These areas are shown as percentages of the total area in figure 4.3.

In order to use this property of the normal curve, since the area proportions are expressed in terms of standard deviation multiples away from the mean, we shall have to recast particular values of a variable in these terms. To do this, we calculate a 'standardised normal variable', otherwise known as a standard score or *z-score*:

$$z = \frac{x - \bar{x}}{\sigma}$$

or, for a sample,

$$z = \frac{x - \bar{x}}{s}$$

where

$x$ is any particular value of the variable
$\bar{x}$ is the mean
$\sigma$ or $s$ is the standard deviation (of a population or sample respectively).

The $z$-score is thus simply the deviation of any given value from the mean, expressed as a multiple of the standard deviation.

Let us now consider how this $z$-score can be used. Suppose that we have measured the times taken by a very large number of people to utter a particular sentence, and have shown these times to be normally distributed (we shall see later how we can test for normality) with a mean of 3.45 sec and a standard deviation of 0.84 sec. Armed with this information, we can answer various questions. What proportion of the (potentially infinite) population of utterance times would be expected to fall below 3 sec? What proportion would lie between 3 and 4 sec? What is the time below which only 1 per cent of the times would be expected to fall? Let us try to answer these questions in order.

Using the formula for $z$ above, we can calculate a $z$-score for a value of 3 sec:

$$z = \frac{3 - 3.45}{0.84} = -0.54.$$

That is, a value of 3 sec lies 0.54 standard deviations below the mean, the fact that it is *below* the mean being reflected in the negative value of $z$. Looking up the table of areas under the normal curve for various values of $z$ (table A2 of appendix 1), we find that a value of 0.54 cuts off a tail containing 0.294 6 of the total area. That is, the proportion of values expected to fall below 3 sec is 0.294 6, or 29.5 per cent.

Now to our second question: what proportion of the times would be expected to lie between 3 and 4 sec? If we can determine the proportion lying above 4 sec, then, since we already know what proportion lies below 3 sec, we can arrive at our answer by subtracting both of these from 100 per cent. The $z$-score for 4 sec is

$$z = \frac{4 - 3.45}{0.84} = 0.66.$$

From the table of areas, a value of 0.66 for $z$ cuts off a tail containing 0.254 6 of the area under the curve. The proportion lying below 3 sec was 0.294 6, so the proportion falling between 3 and 4 sec is

$$100 - 29.46 - 25.46 = 45.1 \text{ per cent.}$$

Finally, what time value is such that only 1 per cent of the times should fall below it? To answer this question, we need to know what $z$-value cuts off a tail containing 0.01 of the area. The table of areas shows that a $z$-score of 2.33 means that 0.009 9 of the area is cut off. If $x$ is the time value we require, then

$$-2.33 = \frac{x - 3.45}{0.84}.$$

Thus

$$x = (-2.33 \times 0.84) + 3.45 = 1.49 \text{ sec.}$$

Note carefully that we use a negative value for $z$ because we are interested in what happens *below* the mean. Readers who are worried by this may find it useful to look at the situation in another way. A $z$-score of 2.33 (irrespective of sign) means that we are talking about a value that is 2.33 standard deviations away from the mean. In our case, this is equivalent to $(2.33 \times 0.84)$ or

1.96 sec. Since we are interested in values below the mean, we must subtract this from the mean value, giving a value of (3.45 − 1.96) or 1.49 sec.

We thus see that the special properties of the normal distribution allow us to make predictions about the proportions of observations lying above, below or between particular limits, defined in terms of multiples of the standard deviation away from the mean.


## 4.3   Testing for normality

It is often necessary to know whether or not a variable is approximately normally distributed. If it is, we can go on to perform calculations of the type just discussed, and we shall also be able to use certain statistical tests considered in later chapters.

One simple way to test roughly for normality is to draw a histogram or frequency polygon of the distribution, to see if it is at least symmetrical and unimodal. We can also test whether the mean, median and mode are close together: as we have seen, these three measures coincide for an exactly normal distribution.

A rather more sophisticated test is based on the fact, discussed earlier, that a fixed proportion of the data will fall between particular values of the variable, if the distribution is normal. We saw that about 34 per cent of the observations should lie between the mean and one standard deviation (on each side of the mean), 47.7 per cent between the mean and two standard deviations, and 49.9 per cent between the mean and three standard deviations. In practice, the last figure means that virtually all the data should lie within three standard deviations of the mean. We can check these theoretical predictions against the actual data for our distribution.

Let us carry out such an exercise for the data from our language teaching experiment, introduced in chapter 1. In chapter 3, we calculated the means and standard deviations for these data. The values were as follows:

*Group A:* mean score        = 14.93 marks;
            standard deviation =   2.49 marks
*Group B:* mean score        = 11.77 marks;
            standard deviation =   3.31 marks

We can now predict that for each group, if the data are indeed normally distributed, about 68 per cent of the scores will lie in the range mean ±1 standard deviation, and about 95 per cent in the range mean ±2 standard deviations. Thus we expect:

*Group A:* about 68% between 12.44 and 17.42;
about 95% between  8.95 and 20.91
*Group B:* about 68% between  8.46 and 15.08;
about 95% between  5.09 and 18.39

Remembering that, for example, 12.44 is very near the lower limit for the interval containing numbers that are rounded to 13, and also that the maximum score on the test is 20, we can translate the above ranges into whole mark scores as follows:

*Group A:* about 68% between 13 and 17;
about 95% between  9 and 20
*Group B:* about 68% between  9 and 15;
about 95% between  5 and 18

The figures actually observed were:

*Group A:* 13–17: 20 out of 30 =  67%;
9–20: 30 out of 30 = 100%
*Group B:*  9–15: 20 out of 30 =  67%;
5–18: 30 out of 30 = 100%

The distribution is perhaps a little short on the extreme values, but this may well be because the sample is quite small: remember that only 5 per cent of the values are expected to lie outside the two standard deviation limit, and in this case such a proportion represents only one or two scores. The predicted and observed proportions within one standard deviation of the mean agree very well indeed, and support our impressions, gained from graphical representations of the distribution, that the variable is approximately normally distributed.

A more exact test for the normality of a distribution will be considered in chapter 9. For most practical purposes, however, the approximate tests discussed above will suffice.

**Exercises**

1   (i)   Explain what is meant in statistics by the term 'normal distribution', and outline its important properties.

(ii)   Suppose that the following scores have been obtained on testing a group of 50 children for proficiency in spoken German. By means of a histogram, and by calculating the proportions of observations lying within certain distances from the mean, show that the scores are approximately normally distributed.

| | | | | |
|---|---|---|---|---|
| 51 | 66 | 84 | 57 | 44 |
| 22 | 67 | 54 | 59 | 48 |
| 69 | 43 | 52 | 65 | 52 |
| 44 | 45 | 52 | 27 | 55 |
| 46 | 50 | 37 | 15 | 59 |
| 61 | 58 | 35 | 51 | 63 |
| 63 | 62 | 45 | 35 | 74 |
| 30 | 20 | 48 | 41 | 28 |
| 73 | 33 | 50 | 49 | 76 |
| 25 | 71 | 55 | 35 | 50 |

(iii)   If a further large sample were taken from the population of students represented by the above group of 50, what percentage of the sample would be expected to score (a) less than 40 marks on the test? (b) between 60 and 70 marks on the test?

2   A group of 100 people have been asked to read a particular sentence, and the maximum sound intensity has been measured for each, in decibels from an arbitrary norm. It is found that the results are normally distributed, with a mean of 23.4 dB and a standard deviation of 5.8 dB. If a further sample were taken from the same population, what proportion of the maximum intensities would be expected to fall

(i)   below 10 dB?
(ii)   above 30 dB?
(iii)   between 20 and 25 dB?

3   The following scores are obtained by 50 subjects on a language aptitude test:

| | | | | | | | | | |
|---|---|---|---|---|---|---|---|---|---|
| 42 | 62 | 44 | 32 | 47 | 42 | 52 | 76 | 36 | 43 |
| 55 | 27 | 46 | 55 | 47 | 28 | 53 | 44 | 15 | 61 |
| 18 | 59 | 58 | 57 | 49 | 55 | 88 | 49 | 50 | 62 |
| 61 | 82 | 66 | 80 | 64 | 50 | 40 | 53 | 28 | 63 |
| 63 | 25 | 58 | 71 | 82 | 52 | 73 | 67 | 58 | 77 |

   (i)   Draw a histogram to show the distribution of the scores.

  (ii)   Calculate the mean and standard deviation of the scores.

 (iii)  Use the values obtained in (ii) to show that the scores are approximately normally distributed.

# 5 Sample statistics and population parameters: estimation

## 5.1 Introduction

We have seen that when the population in which we are interested is potentially infinite, or so large that it would be difficult to study it exhaustively, we rely on samples selected from the population. Measures calculated on the basis of samples are thus estimates of the corresponding population parameters. Having, say, calculated the mean for one or more samples from our population, we cannot claim that this is the true mean for the whole population; indeed, we cannot say exactly what the population mean is. What we can do, however, as we shall see in this chapter, is to calculate a range of values within which we can have a certain degree of confidence that the true population parameter lies.

## 5.2 The sampling distribution of the mean

Let us suppose that we are interested in the syntactic complexity of sentences in a large body of texts and have elaborated a measure of such complexity, expressed as an index. We might select a sample of 50 sentences from the texts and calculate a mean value for the complexity index. Let us suppose that the mean for our sample is 58.2. If we now took a further 50 sentences from the same population, it is rather unlikely that their mean complexity index would be exactly 58.2: it might be 57.3, or 59.6, or 61.4, and so on. The mean for each sample is merely an estimate of the mean index for the whole corpus. Some samples of 50 sentences would have means below the true population mean, others would have means above it. If we obtained means for a large number of samples, we could plot their frequency distribution, which would tend towards a smooth curve known as the *sampling distribution of the mean* for that population. This distribution has certain important properties, as illustrated in figures 5.1 and 5.2.

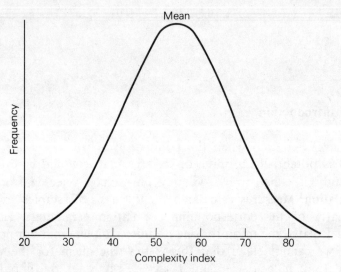

**Figure 5.1**    **Frequency distribution for population**

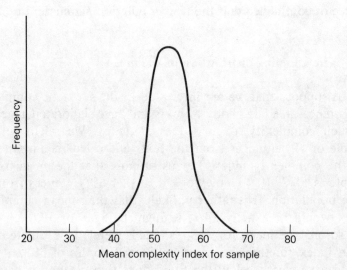

**Figure 5.2**    **Sampling distribution of the mean**

Firstly, the sampling distribution is normal. Strictly speaking, this is true only when the distribution of scores in the population itself is normal. However, it can be shown that, whatever the shape of the distribution for the parent population, the distribution of sample means is approximately normal, provided the samples are reasonably large (say, above 30). This important finding is known as the 'central limit theorem'.

Secondly, the mean of the sampling distribution is equal to the mean for the population. This is what we should expect, since in a large number of samples deviations below the true population mean will tend to cancel out those above the mean.

Thirdly, the variability of the means is smaller than that of the raw scores. This is again predictable on common-sense grounds. When considering individual scores, we may well find some which are considerably removed from the mean. In taking the mean of a number of observations, however, the effect of such 'freak' scores will be diluted by the more typical ones. The variability of the means can be measured by the standard deviation of the sampling distribution, which is called the *standard error of the mean*. Obviously, the larger the sample size, the more dilution of untypical scores there will be, and the more the sample means will cluster around the population mean, so decreasing the standard error. The precise relationship between the standard error, the standard deviation of scores in the population and the sample size is as follows:

$$\text{standard error} = \frac{\sigma}{\sqrt{N}}$$

where

$\sigma$ is the population standard deviation
$N$ is the sample size.

Normally, we have to estimate the population standard deviation from that of a sample, $s$. We then have:

$$\text{standard error} = \frac{s}{\sqrt{N}}.$$

Note that the standard error does not decrease in direct proportion to the sample size, but rather in proportion to the square root of $N$. This means that in order to halve the standard error, we should have to take a sample which was not twice, but four times as big.

## 5.3    Interpreting the standard error: confidence limits

Let us return to our syntactic complexity investigation. With a sample of 50 sentences, we had a mean of 58.2 for the complexity index. Let us also assume that the observed standard deviation of scores in the sample was 23.6. We can now calculate the standard error of the mean:

$$\text{standard error} = \frac{s}{\sqrt{N}} = \frac{23.6}{\sqrt{50}} = 3.3.$$

We might now quote the mean as $58.2 \pm 3.3$. In so doing, we are giving what is called a 'point estimate' of the mean, together with an indication of the range of error. But how, exactly, are we to interpret the standard error?

Let us call the true population mean $\mu$, as is conventional. The deviation of the sample mean from this population mean is then $(58.2 - \mu)$, which may be positive or negative according to whether the sample mean is above or below that for the population. If we now divide this by the standard deviation of the sampling distribution (which, as we have seen, is the standard error), we obtain a $z$-score (or 'standardised score') of the kind discussed in relation to the normal curve in section 4.2:

$$z = \frac{58.2 - \mu}{3.3}.$$

For large values of the sample size, $N$ (in practice, for $N = 30$ or above), $z$ is distributed normally, and we can therefore use the table of areas under the normal curve to calculate the probability of obtaining a value of $z$ equal to or greater than any given value. It will be seen from table A2 of appendix 1 that a $z$-score of 1.96 cuts off a tail containing 0.025 of the area under the curve. For a positive $z$-score, this tail will be cut off on the positive side of the curve, and since the curve is symmetrical, a $z$-score of $-1.96$ like-

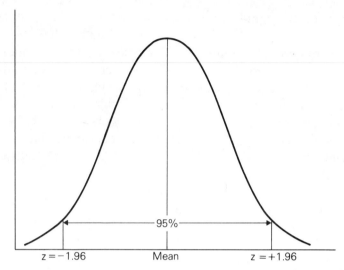

**Figure 5.3**   $z$-scores enclosing 95 per cent of the area under the normal curve

wise cuts off 0.025 of the area, this time on the negative side. Between the $z$-scores of $-1.96$ and $+1.96$, therefore, lies 95 per cent of the area under the curve, as shown in figure 5.3. In other words, there is a 95 per cent probability of getting a $z$-score between $-1.96$ and $+1.96$. So we can be 95 per cent sure that $\mu$ lies in the range defined by

$$-1.96 \leqslant \frac{58.2 - \mu}{3.3} \leqslant +1.96$$

or

$$-(3.3 \times 1.96) \leqslant 58.2 - \mu \leqslant +(3.3 \times 1.96)$$

or

$$-6.5 \leqslant 58.2 - \mu \leqslant +6.5$$

or

$$51.7 \leqslant \mu \leqslant 64.7.$$

Thus we can be 95 per cent confident in claiming that the true mean syntactic complexity for the whole population of sentences lies between 51.7 and 64.7. We can put this in another way: if we were to obtain a large number of samples, we should expect the mean to lie between 51.7 and 64.7 in 95 per cent of them. We are now giving an 'interval estimate' of the mean, and 51.7 and 64.7 are known as the 95 per cent *confidence limits* for the mean.

It can be seen from the above fully worked calculation that there is an easy way of working out the confidence limits, given the sample mean and the standard error. The 95 per cent confidence limits are

sample mean $\pm$ (1.96 $\times$ standard error)

where 1.96 is the 'critical value' for 95 per cent confidence.

If we wished to set a different percentage confidence, we should need to use a different value for the critical value of $z$. For instance, if we wanted to be 99 per cent certain of including the true mean within our confidence limits, we should have to use $z = 2.58$, which cuts off 0.005 of the area under the normal curve on each side. We then have as 99 per cent confidence limits

sample mean $\pm$ (2.58 $\times$ standard error).

For our syntactic complexity data, we calculate:

lower 99% confidence limit = $58.2 - (2.58 \times 3.3) = 49.7$
upper 99% confidence limit = $58.2 + (2.58 \times 3.3) = 66.7$.

These are further apart than the limits calculated for 95 per cent confidence, and this is only to be expected, since we have increased our degree of certainty. The limits could, of course, be narrowed by increasing the sample size. For instance, with a sample size of 100, and assuming our original standard deviation, we have

$$\text{standard error} = \frac{23.6}{\sqrt{100}} = 2.36$$

99% confidence limits = $58.2 \pm (2.58 \times 2.36)$

$$= 58.2 \pm 6.1 = 52.1 \text{ to } 64.3.$$

## 5.4   Estimation from small samples: the *t* distribution

We have seen that the ratio

$$z = \frac{\bar{x} - \mu}{\text{standard error}}$$

is normally distributed for large values of *N*. For sample sizes of less than about 30, however, the distribution is not normal, and we must refer to the so-called *t distribution* rather than to the normal curve. The shape of this distribution is not fixed, but depends on the number of *degrees of freedom* involved in the calculation of the standard deviation. This is a very important concept, which we shall need again when we discuss statistical testing of hypotheses. The number of degrees of freedom is the number of values of the variable which are free to vary. Now, the calculation of a standard deviation involves using the value of the mean, and of each score. If there are *N* scores, only $(N-1)$ of them are free to vary for a given mean, since the other one must be such as to contribute just enough to the value of the mean. Thus, the number of degrees of freedom in calculating a standard deviation, and hence the number used in our present application of the *t* distribution, is $(N-1)$. This, by the way, is why we divide $\Sigma(x - \bar{x})^2$ by $(N-1)$ rather than *N* in order to obtain an unbiased estimate of the variance and standard deviation (see section 3.3.5). Tables of *t* values (see table A3 of appendix 1) give the probability of exceeding given values of *t* for particular numbers of degrees of freedom. We calculate *t* exactly as we would calculate *z* for a larger sample, then refer to the table of *t* values, using the appropriate number of degrees of freedom.

There is one more complication concerning the use of the *t* table: it gives two sets of probabilities, one for 'one-tailed' tests and another for 'two-tailed' tests. We shall go into this important distinction more fully in chapter 6. For now, we need note only that the probability values for the two-tailed situation take into account the areas of both tails of the curve, as the term suggests, while the one-tailed values take account of just one tail. For example, if we look up the critical value of *t* for a probability of 0.05, and for a given number of degrees of freedom, we shall

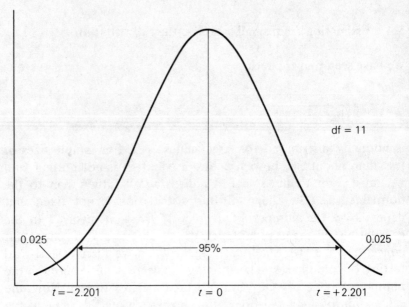

**Figure 5.4**    *t* values between which 95 per cent of the area under the curve
lies, for 11 degrees of freedom

obtain, using the two-tailed probabilities, that *t* value beyond
which 0.025 of the area lies on each side of the curve, making 0.05
in all. For 11 degrees of freedom, for instance, the critical value
of *t* is 2.201, so that we have the situation illustrated diagrammatically in figure 5.4.

Let us now work through an example of the use of the *t* distribution in estimation from a small sample. Suppose that the times
taken to detransform a sentence into its simplest form have been
measured for 15 subjects, with the following results: 4.81, 3.90,
5.21, 4.86, 3.25, 4.20, 4.52, 3.65, 3.80, 4.12, 4.20, 5.08, 4.02,
3.84, 4.39 sec. We wish to find the 95 per cent confidence limits
for the true mean time for the population from which the sample
is drawn. First, we calculate the mean and standard deviation:

$$\bar{x} = \frac{\Sigma x}{N} = \frac{63.85}{15} = 4.26 \text{ sec}$$

$$s = \sqrt{\frac{\Sigma x^2 - (\Sigma x)^2/N}{N-1}} = \sqrt{\frac{276.10 - (63.85)^2/15}{14}} = 0.56 \text{ sec.}$$

We now compute the standard error:

$$\text{standard error} = \frac{s}{\sqrt{N}} = \frac{0.56}{\sqrt{15}} = 0.14\,\text{sec.}$$

This value can now be used in an expression for the confidence limits which is precisely analogous to that for situations where the normal distribution is appropriate:

confidence limits = sample mean

$\pm$ (critical value of $t$ $\times$ standard error).

From table A3 of appendix 1, the critical value of $t$ for a probability of 0.05 and 14 (that is, $N-1$) degrees of freedom is 2.145, using the two-tailed probabilities. We therefore have

95% confidence limits = $4.26 \pm (2.145 \times 0.14)$

$= 4.26 \pm 0.30 = 3.96$ to $4.56\,\text{sec.}$

We can thus be 95 per cent certain that the true mean lies between 3.96 and 4.56 sec for the population concerned.

## 5.5 Confidence limits for proportions

Principles similar to those discussed above for means can also be applied to the proportion of items in a population having a particular property. Let us imagine that we have taken a random sample of 500 finite verbs from a text, and found that 150 of these (that is, 0.3 or 30 per cent) have present tense form. How can we set confidence limits for the proportion of present tense finite verbs in the whole text, the population from which the sample is taken?

It can be shown that the standard error of a proportion is given by:

$$\text{standard error} = \sqrt{\frac{p(1-p)}{N}}$$

where

> $p$ is the proportion in the sample
> $N$ is the sample size.

Thus for our sample of 500 finite verbs, we have:

$$\text{standard error} = \sqrt{\frac{0.30(1-0.30)}{500}} = \sqrt{\frac{0.30\times0.70}{500}}$$

$$= 0.02 \text{ or } 2\%.$$

Provided that $N$ is large, or that $p$ is quite close to 0.5, or both, the sampling distribution of a proportion is approximately normal, and we can apply the same reasoning as was discussed in section 5.3 in relation to the mean. We are generally safe in doing this if the product of $N$ and $p$ (or of $N$ and $(1-p)$ if this is smaller) is at least 5. For our data, the product is equal to $(500\times0.3)$ or 150, so we may assume normality of the sampling distribution. We therefore have:

$$95\% \text{ confidence limits} = \text{proportion in sample}$$

$$\pm\,(1.96\times\text{standard error})$$

$$= 0.30\pm(1.96\times0.02)$$

$$= 0.30\pm0.04 = 0.26 \text{ to } 0.34.$$

We can thus be 95 per cent confident that the proportion of present tense finite verbs in the population lies between 26 and 34 per cent.

## 5.6    Estimating required sample sizes

We have used the standard error to compute confidence limits for a particular size of sample. We can also use it the other way round, to calculate the size of sample required in order to estimate a population parameter to within a given degree of accuracy.

In the above paragraph there are 46 word tokens, of which 11 are two-letter words. The proportion of such words is thus 11/46 or 0.24. How big a sample of words should we need in order to be 95 per cent confident that we had measured the proportion to within an accuracy of 1 per cent? Here, we are allowing ourselves a margin of error of 1 per cent, or 0.01. But this is merely the range, on either side of the true proportion, specified by the confidence limits for our chosen confidence level of 95 per cent. Thus:

$$\text{error tolerated} = 1.96 \times \text{standard error}.$$

For our case, then,

$$0.01 = 1.96 \times \text{standard error}$$

or

$$\text{standard error} = \frac{0.01}{1.96}.$$

But we know that the standard error of a proportion is given by

$$\text{standard error} = \sqrt{\frac{p(1-p)}{N}}.$$

Since $p = 0.24$ in our case, we have

$$\frac{0.01}{1.96} = \sqrt{\frac{0.24 \times (1-0.24)}{N}}$$

where $N$ is the required sample size. Squaring both sides,

$$\left(\frac{0.01}{1.96}\right)^2 = \frac{0.24 \times 0.76}{N}$$

and

$$N = \frac{0.24 \times 0.76}{(0.01/1.96)^2} = 7\,007.$$

We therefore need a sample of about 7 000 words in order to estimate the proportion with the required degree of accuracy.

**Exercises**

1   A sample of 100 sentences, selected to be representative of a larger corpus of sentences, has a mean length of 14.21 words and a standard deviation of 6.87 words. Calculate the standard error of the mean, and the 95 per cent confidence limits for the mean.

2   Twenty subjects are asked to read a sentence on to tape, and the length of pause at a particular point in the sentence measured in milliseconds, with the following results:

| 25 | 32 | 30 | 20 | 15 | 34 | 36 | 28 | 22 | 31 |
|----|----|----|----|----|----|----|----|----|----|
| 27 | 33 | 26 | 19 | 21 | 20 | 26 | 35 | 17 | 24 |

Calculate (i) the mean pause length, (ii) the standard deviation, (iii) the standard error of the mean, (iv) the 95 per cent confidence limits for the mean. Comment on the results.

3   The following are the times (in seconds) taken for a group of 30 subjects to carry out the detransformation of a sentence into its simplest form:

| 0.55 | 0.56 | 0.52 | 0.59 | 0.51 | 0.50 |
|------|------|------|------|------|------|
| 0.42 | 0.41 | 0.37 | 0.22 | 0.24 | 0.41 |
| 0.49 | 0.59 | 0.75 | 0.65 | 0.63 | 0.61 |
| 0.72 | 0.77 | 0.76 | 0.39 | 0.26 | 0.68 |
| 0.30 | 0.32 | 0.44 | 0.61 | 0.54 | 0.47 |

Calculate (i) the mean, (ii) the standard deviation, (iii) the standard error of the mean, (iv) the 99 per cent confidence limits for the mean.

4   A random sample of 300 finite verbs is taken from a text, and it is found that 63 of these are auxiliaries. Calculate the 95 per cent confidence limits for the proportion of finite verbs which are auxiliaries in the text as a whole.

5   Using the data in question 4, calculate the size of the sample of finite verbs which would be required in order to estimate the proportion of auxiliaries to within an accuracy of 1 per cent, with 95 per cent confidence.

# 6 Project design and hypothesis testing: basic principles

## 1.1 Introduction

So far, we have concentrated on the methods available for summarising and describing data, and for estimating population parameters from sample statistics. We have said very little about the use of statistical techniques for testing hypotheses about the differences between sets of data. It is with this important area that most of the remainder of this book will be concerned. In this chapter, the basic principles underlying statistical testing are examined. These are inextricably bound up with the question of project design, and it is with this that we begin our discussion.

## 6.2 The design of investigations

### 6.2.1 Experimental and observational studies

We may distinguish two fundamental types of scientific investigation, in linguistics as in other social and natural sciences. *Experimental studies* are those in which the investigator deliberately manipulates some factor(s) or circumstance(s) in order to test the effect on some other phenomenon. The language teaching project we have made use of in our discussion of descriptive statistics is an example of an experimental study. The investigator deliberately manipulates the independent variable (teaching method) and measures the effect on the dependent variable (proficiency, as assessed by a test). A second example of an experimental study might involve the principled varying of the syntactic complexity (defined in some precise way) of sentences presented to human subjects, and the testing of the accuracy with which the subjects can recall the sentences after a given time. Again, we have deliberately altered one factor (syntactic complexity) in order to test its effect on another (accuracy of recall).

Experimental studies are extremely common in the natural and physical sciences and are, as we have seen, also suitable for some types of linguistic investigation. Often, however, the linguist, psychologist or sociologist is interested in areas where he cannot deliberately manipulate the independent variable. Consider, for instance, an investigation into the relationship between the length of words (measured in letters, syllables or whatever) and the frequency of their use in a particular register of English. Here, there is no question of manipulating the word length: all we can do is collect samples of the kind of English we are interested in, measure the lengths and frequencies of the words they contain, and attempt to deduce some relationship between them. We still have an independent variable (word length) and a dependent variable (frequency), but the investigator is no longer in control of the independent variable. Studies of this kind are called *observational* or *correlational studies*.

## 6.2.2   *Sources of unwanted variation, and their minimisation*

In some ways, experimental studies are more satisfactory than observational studies. Not only does the experimenter have precise control over the independent variable, but he can also take steps to design his experiment in such a way that the effects of other variables irrelevant to his aims are minimised, so that he can more confidently claim that the effects he observes are indeed due to the independent variable. In an observational study, where the data are simply there for the investigator to analyse, there is a greater likelihood of interference from extraneous 'irrelevant' variables, although such interference can be lessened by judicious selection of the data in the first place. In many situations of interest to the linguist, however, only observational studies are possible, and we must simply be as rigorous as we can.

Even in an experimental study, we cannot hope to remove entirely the effects of irrelevant variables. What we must at all costs try to eliminate is the *systematic* variation of such factors. For instance, going back to our language teaching methods experiment, if we were to allocate all the male subjects in our investigation to one teaching method and all the female subjects to the other, we should not know whether to attribute any differences in the performance of the two groups to the method variable or to the sex variable, the latter of which is 'irrelevant' in the sense that we are not trying to measure its effects. We must therefore try to ensure that the effects of irrelevant variables operate randomly over our sample of subjects, and also we must try to minimise such effects, since they will cause greater variability in the results obtained, with a consequent loss of confidence in the statements we can make.

There are two types of irrelevant variable: *subject variables*, concerned with the properties of the experimental subjects themselves (in our language teaching experiment, such variables would include the age, sex and motivation of the learners); and *situational variables*, concerned with the conditions under which the experiment is carried out (for example, the teachers taking the classes, the physical conditions in the classrooms and so on).

Subject variables can be controlled in one of three ways. The strictest control is achieved where the same subjects can be used for the two (or more) conditions involved in the experiment: this is the so-called *repeated measures* design, which eliminates all the effects of subject variables for a particular pair (or set) of measurements. This design could be used, for example, in our experiment to determine the effect of syntactic complexity on sentence recall; it could obviously not be used, however, in the case of the language teaching experiment, since there is no question of 'relearning' a particular language skill by another method. Furthermore, the repeated measures design brings its own dangers, in the form of possible effects arising from the order in which the tasks are performed in the experiment; for it is possible that human beings may be more fatigued or bored by one condition of an experiment than by another, or that the practice acquired in the first task may be helpful in performance of the second. Some order effects, though not all, can be minimised by having half the group do the tasks in one order and half in the reverse order, but in general it is best to avoid this design with human subjects if order effects are likely to be significant.

A second way of controlling subject variables is by selecting pairs of subjects very closely matched on particular subject variables. This is the so-called *matched subjects* design. In our language teaching experiment, for example, we could try to select pairs of learners matched for age, sex, IQ and motivation, and allocate one member of each pair to each group by randomisation methods such as those discussed in section 1.2. There are two major difficulties with this design: it is often hard to know what variables to control for; and it is not easy to find suitable matched pairs, especially if we are dealing with a ready-made group such as a school class.

The third way of controlling subject variables, the *independent groups* design, is the most flexible and most widely used, though it gives the least control over irrelevant factors. Here, the subjects (which will, in the ideal case, be a random sample from the population concerned) are themselves allocated to the two (or more) conditions in a strictly random manner. Sometimes, rather than using simple randomisation and hoping that irrelevant variables will cancel out, it is better to perform a stratified randomising operation of the kind described in section 1.2; for instance, we could ensure that our groups contained equal numbers of males and females, or equal numbers of learners from particular IQ bands, but that within these constraints the allocation of subjects was strictly random.

The control of situational variables may be achieved in part by attempting to hold such variables constant (for example, by using the same teacher for both classes throughout the period of our language teaching experiment), or making sure that they are experienced equally by all subjects (for example, by using two teachers for the same lengths of time with both classes). In the case of experimental testing, we can minimise the effects of variation in situational conditions by testing the sample of subjects in random order.

### 6.2.3   A caveat

The importance of well thought out design cannot be too strongly emphasised. No amount of sophisticated statistical juggling will produce valid results from a badly designed investigation, although some 'tidying up' may be possible. Neither will statistical significance tell us anything about the worth or usefulness of the findings: the investigators themselves must bear responsibility for deciding what is worth investigating.

### 6.3   Hypothesis testing

### 6.3.1   The need for statistical tests of significance

If we have demonstrated a difference in, say, the means or medians for two sets of data, can we not just say that one is indeed greater than the other, and leave it at that? This would, in fact, be most unwise, and would show a lack of understanding of the nature of statistical inference. To see why, let us return once more to the language teaching experiment.

In chapter 3 we saw that the mean scores for groups A and B in the experiment were 14.93 and 11.77, respectively. But if we look at the frequency polygon for the two distributions (figure 2.6), we see that there is considerable overlap between them. Some of the better students in group B have obtained higher scores than some of the weaker ones in group A. In view of this, we cannot be absolutely sure, without further testing, that the observed difference in means can be attributed to the teaching methods used with the two groups, rather than to a slight imbalance in irrelevant variables. It may be that, despite our best efforts to select samples appropriately, there are certain differences between the groups which are due merely to the inherent variability of samples rather than to teaching method.

The aim of statistical tests of significance is to show whether or not the observed differences between sets of data could reasonably have been expected to occur 'by chance' (that is, owing to sampling variation) or whether, on the contrary, they are most probably due to the alteration in the variable whose effect is being investigated. In what follows, we shall be more precise about what we mean by 'reasonably' and 'most probably' in the above formulation.

## 6.3.2 *The null hypothesis and alternative hypothesis*

It is important to be very clear about exactly what it is that we are testing in 'hypothesis testing'. The first step is to set up what is called the *null hypothesis*. This is a precise statement about some value or set of values, and is usually phrased in the form, 'there is no difference between the values of such-and-such a parameter in the populations from which the samples were drawn'; hence the term 'null'. For the language teaching experiment our null hypothesis would be: 'there is no difference between the means in the populations from which the two groups of scores were drawn.' The null hypothesis is usually symbolised as $H_0$, so that we could write:

$$H_0: \mu_A - \mu_B = 0 \quad or \quad \mu_A = \mu_B.$$

Contrasting with the null hypothesis is the investigator's *alternative hypothesis* (sometimes called the *experimental hypothesis*). In the case of the language teaching experiment, the alternative hypothesis could be simply that $\mu_A$ is not equal to $\mu_B$, or that $\mu_A$ is greater than $\mu_B$, or that $\mu_B$ is greater than $\mu_A$. (The consequences, for the test procedure, of selecting one of these alternatives rather than another will be discussed in section 6.3.5.) The alternative hypothesis is usually symbolised as $H_1$, so that, for the first of the possibilities mentioned above, we can write

$$H_1: \mu_A \neq \mu_B.$$

The strategy of hypothesis testing is to try to accumulate enough evidence to reject the null hypothesis, rather than to try to support any of the possible alternative hypotheses directly. What we must do is to calculate, by means of some suitable procedure, a *test statistic* which will allow us to find the probability of obtaining the results we have observed, on the assumption that the null hypothesis is true. For the language teaching experiment the question to be answered would be: 'under the null hypothesis that there is no difference in the means of the populations of scores from which the two samples were drawn, what is the probability of obtaining sample means differing by at least the observed amount?' If there is only a very small probability of getting the observed difference in sample means, then we can reject the null hypothesis, and accept our alternative hypothesis (for instance, that there *is* a difference in the means for the populations, which is attributable to teaching method). If the probability of obtaining the observed results is quite high, we cannot reject the null hypothesis: the two samples may well be from populations with identical means.

It is extremely important to realise that we can never *prove conclusively* that the null hypothesis is incorrect, or that any alternative hypothesis is correct. There is always a chance (maybe a very small one) that the differences we observe are indeed due to sampling variation and not to the independent variable. All we can do is try to show that the probability of this being so is very small. But how small does the probability have to be before we can reject the null hypothesis? This is the question to which we now turn.

### 6.3.3 Significance levels

The probability level below which we are willing to treat our observed differences as significant is called the *significance level* of a test. For instance, if we are willing to reject the null hypothesis if the probability ($p$) of obtaining our observed difference (or a more extreme one) is smaller than or equal to 0.05, then we choose a significance level of 0.05, usually written as $p \leqslant 0.05$, and often referred to as 'the 5 per cent level'. In the physical sciences, where measurements can often be made to a high degree of accuracy, and where (as, for example, in testing drugs for human use) the practical consequences of making a wrong decision might be serious, a level of $p \leqslant 0.01$ or even $p \leqslant 0.001$ may be chosen, meaning that the null hypothesis will be rejected only if there is at most a 1 in 100 (or 1 in 1 000) chance of getting the observed results under the null hypothesis. In linguistics and other socially oriented sciences, where measurement is often less exact, a level of $p \leqslant 0.05$ is quite common. Much depends on the purpose for which the testing is being carried out. If, for instance, we are trying to refute some well established theory, then we may well choose a rather stringent significance level of 1 per cent or even 0.1 per cent. If, on the other hand, we are looking for suggestive evidence on which to decide whether further work may be useful, a 5 per cent or even a 10 per cent ($p \leqslant 0.1$) level may suffice. Differences that are significant at the 5 per cent level are often said to be simply 'significant', while those at the 1 per cent level are 'highly significant', and those at the 0.1 per cent level 'very highly significant'; however, it is always best to give precise numerical significance levels.

For any particular test, and any selected significance level, there will be a *critical value* of the test statistic, which delimits a *critical region* within which the value of the statistic must fall if the observed differences are to be regarded as statistically significant at that level. If the value of the test statistic calculated for the data lies well outside the critical region, the null hypothesis cannot be rejected. If it lies just outside, very close to the critical value, the null hypothesis still cannot be rejected for that particular set of observations, but the investigator may well be advised to repeat the study with larger samples, in the hope of achieving significance.

## 6.3.4    Types of error in significance testing

When we make a decision to reject or accept the null hypothesis, there are two kinds of error we can make. We may reject $H_0$ when in fact it is true, or we may accept $H_0$ when it is false. The probability of making the first kind of error, known as the 'type I error' and symbolised as $\alpha$, is equal to the significance level, as we should expect; after all, the significance level represents the maximum acceptable probability of our results actually being due to sampling error, even though we claim a significant difference. The second kind of error ('type II'), symbolised as $\beta$, represents the situation where we are being too cautious, in claiming that we have insufficient evidence to refute $H_0$, when in fact $H_0$ is untrue. The factors affecting the value of $\beta$ are beyond the scope of our discussion. One fact, however, is of some importance: as the value of $\alpha$ decreases, that of $\beta$ increases. That is, the danger of making a type II error is greater for a significance level of $p \leqslant 0.01$ than for $p \leqslant 0.05$, and even greater still for a level of $p \leqslant 0.001$. The significance levels most commonly used are in fact a compromise between the two types of possible error.

## 6.3.5    Directional (one-tailed) and non-directional (two-tailed) tests

In discussing the null and alternative hypotheses in section 6.3.2, we pointed out that a number of alternative hypotheses might correspond to a particular null hypothesis. For our language teaching experiment, the following possibilities exist:

$H_1: \mu_A \neq \mu_B$

$H_1: \mu_A > \mu_B$

$H_1: \mu_B > \mu_A.$

In the first of these cases, we are predicting that there is a difference in the means, but are not claiming anything about the direction of the difference. This is, then, an example of a *non-directional* prediction. The other two alternative hypotheses, on the other hand, make *directional* predictions, since they claim that one specified population has a higher mean than the other.

To understand the consequences of such predictions for the carrying out of significance tests, we need to realise that the possible values which can be taken by a test statistic will form a frequency distribution, to which the statistical tables used in significance testing will refer. For instance, in chapter 7 we shall describe tests using the normal distribution and also the $t$ distribution, which we met when discussing estimation from small samples in section 5.4. The probability of obtaining a value of the test statistic falling outside a specified range will be equal to the proportion of the area under the curve cut off by vertical lines drawn at the extremes of that range – a line of argument with which we are already familiar from earlier work. Now, if we are making a prediction about the direction of the difference between two population parameters, only one tail of the distribution curve will be relevant; hence, directional tests are often called 'one-tailed' tests. On the other hand, if we are making no prediction about the direction of the difference, we must take into account both tails of the curve, the one corresponding to the situation where, for instance, $\mu_A > \mu_B$, the other to the situation where $\mu_B > \mu_A$; non-directional tests are therefore often said to be 'two-tailed'.

If, for example, we choose a significance level of $p \leqslant 0.05$, this means that for a directional test the critical value of our test statistic will cut off a single tail containing 0.05 of the area under the curve; while for a non-directional test the area cut off will be split between the two tails, each with 0.025 of the total area under the curve. This is shown diagrammatically in figure 6.1. As can be seen, a higher value of the test statistic must be attained for a non-directional, or two-tailed, test than for a directional (one-tailed) test. This makes sense if we reflect that in a directional test we are, as it were, feeding more information in (the direction as well as the existence of a difference), so that, in return, we can allow ourselves to claim significance at a lower value of the test statistic than would be required if we simply predicted a difference in the population parameters.

The choice of a directional or a non-directional test depends on the circumstances under which the investigation is conducted. In our language teaching experiment, for instance, we may already have some preliminary evidence that the language laboratory increases proficiency more than traditional teaching. In this case a directional test, with the alternative hypothesis $\mu_A > \mu_B$, would

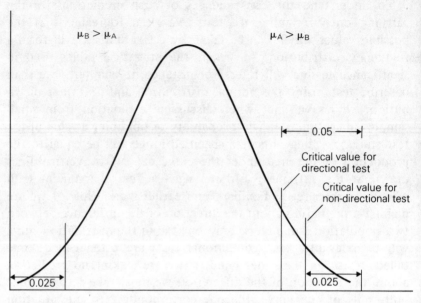

**Figure 6.1    Critical values for directional and non-directional tests**

be appropriate. If, on the other hand, we have no good reason to believe that one particular group will perform better than the other, then a non-directional test should be used.

### 6.3.6    Choosing a test

The setting up of the null hypothesis and an alternative hypothesis, the choice of an appropriate significance level and the decision whether to use a directional or a non-directional test are common to the whole range of specific types of significance test. The choice of a particular test depends on three major factors:

1    the level of measurement of the variable concerned (interval/ratio, ordinal, nominal);
2    the characteristics of the frequency distribution;
3    the type of design used for the study.

For data with ratio or interval levels of measurement, *parametric tests* are often appropriate. These take into account the absolute magnitude of each observation, and so make maximum use of the information available. For this reason, they are quite 'powerful', in the sense that they can detect quite small true differences, given a reasonable sample size. Unfortunately, parametric tests make certain assumptions about the nature of the frequency distributions for the populations concerned. The principal assumption is that the populations have a normal distribution of the variable, although this requirement may be relaxed in certain circumstances, because of the central limit theorem (see section 5.2), which, as readers may remember, states that the sampling distribution of the mean is approximately normal even where the distribution within the original population is not normal, provided that the sample size is large. Some parametric tests also assume that the populations have equal variances.

Where the requirements of a parametric test are not fulfilled, a *non-parametric test* will be more appropriate. Such tests make no assumptions about the shapes or variances of the distributions involved. Some are based on ranking, and so are generally suitable for ordinal data; others are appropriate for nominal data. None of these non-parametric tests, however, takes into account the absolute magnitude of each observation, so that the information used is less than in a parametric test, and the discriminatory power generally rather lower, though in some cases the differences are minimal. A further advantage of non-parametric tests is that the computational effort involved is usually smaller than for parametric tests. Since many problems in linguistic statistics have characteristics which make parametric tests inappropriate, non-parametric methods are of great value in this area. Because of the relative ease of computation, and the (at times) rather small sacrifice in power involved, non-parametric tests are sometimes used in preference to parametric tests even when the conditions for the latter are satisfied.

The final factor involved in the selection of a significance test is the design of the investigation. Where a repeated measures or matched subjects design is used, the pair of measurements obtained for each subject or matched pair of subjects may be *correlated*, in that each may reflect some characteristic of the particular subject in a repeated measures design, or some common characteristic of the pair in a matched subjects design (the concept of correlation will be discussed further in chapter 11). This possible correlation is reflected in the manner of calculating the test statistic, which will be different from that used for independent samples. Both parametric and non-parametric tests are available for each type of situation. Table 6.1 summarises the tests to be discussed in the following chapters.

**Table 6.1   Categorisation of tests**

|  | Independent samples | Correlated samples |
|---|---|---|
| Parametric | z-test<br>t-test for independent samples | t-test for correlated samples |
| Non-parametric | Mann–Whitney U-test<br>Chi-square test | Wilcoxon test<br>Sign test |

*6.3.7   Summary of procedure for hypothesis testing*

We may summarise the steps to be taken in hypothesis testing as follows.

1   State the null hypothesis and the alternative hypothesis, making clear whether the latter is directional or non-directional.

2   Decide on an appropriate significance level, according to the nature and purpose of the investigation.

3   Select an appropriate test, according to:
   (i)    the level of measurement of the data;
   (ii)   the characteristics of the distribution;
   (iii)  the design of the investigation.

4   Calculate the value of the test statistic for the data, and compare with the critical value for the significance level selected, and for a directional or non-directional test, as appropriate. If the calculated value lies inside the critical region, reject the null hypothesis and accept the alternative hypothesis. If the calculated value lies outside the critical region, the null hypothesis cannot be rejected.

**Exercises**

1   Describe in detail how you would set up and conduct an experiment to determine the effect of grammatical mood and choice of modal verb on the relative politeness of forms such as the following, used as a means of getting someone to shut a door:

You must shut the door.
You can shut the door.

You will shut the door.
Can you shut the door?
Will you shut the door?
Shut the door, will you?

Pay particular attention to the methodological problems involved, and to possible solutions to these problems.

2  (i)   What is a statistical test?
   (ii)  Why are such tests needed?
   (iii) What factors determine the selection of an appropriate test?

# 7 Parametric tests of significance

## 7.1 Introduction

Let us first remind ourselves of the conditions for the applicability of parametric tests.

1. The data must have at least an interval level of measurement.
2. The tests are, strictly speaking, applicable only where the populations from which the samples are taken are normal, though this requirement can be relaxed in the case of large samples. Some tests also require the variances of the populations to be approximately equal.

In this chapter we shall devote most of our attention to tests for the significance of differences between means, for independent and for correlated samples. We shall then discuss briefly how we may test the significance of differences between the proportions of some characteristic in two samples.

## 7.2 Testing the significance of differences between two means

### 7.2.1 Tests for independent samples

#### 7.2.1.1 The z-test for large samples

Let us suppose that we have two independently drawn samples, with means $\bar{x}_1$ and $\bar{x}_2$ for some particular variable, and that we wish to know whether the means differ significantly at, say, the $p \leqslant 0.05$ level. That is, we are asking the question, 'If we claim that the means of the populations from which the samples were drawn differ, shall we have at least a 95 per cent chance of being right?' The null hypothesis is that there is no difference between the population means. Possible alternative hypotheses are that there is a difference in the population means (that is, $\mu_1 \neq \mu_2$), or that $\mu_1 > \mu_2$, or that $\mu_2 > \mu_1$. What we need to calculate, then, is the probability that the two samples could have been drawn from populations with the same mean, the differences arising merely from sampling variability. In other words, we need to know the probability that two samples from populations with the same mean could have means differing by as much as $(\bar{x}_1 - \bar{x}_2)$.

We saw in section 5.2 that the sampling distribution of the means for a large number of samples from a population was normal, with a standard deviation (the standard error) given by

$$\text{standard error} = \frac{\sigma}{\sqrt{N}}$$

where

$\sigma$ is the population standard deviation
$N$ is the sample size.

What we now need, however, is not the standard error of a single mean, but the standard error of the difference between two means. Since this is the standard deviation of the distribution of differences between means, we should be able to use it to find the probability of obtaining a difference in means equal to or larger than any particular value. We should expect the standard error of the difference to be larger than that for a single mean, since the variability of *two* means is involved. In fact, it can be shown that provided $N_1$ and $N_2$ are large, the following relationship is a good approximation even for non-normal populations:

$$\text{standard error of difference} = \sqrt{\sigma_1^2/N_1 + \sigma_2^2/N_2}$$

where

$\sigma_1^2, \sigma_2^2$ are variances of populations 1 and 2
$N_1$ and $N_2$ are sizes of samples 1 and 2.

Unfortunately, we do not know the population variances in most cases, so we must estimate them from the variances of our samples. Provided that $N_1$ and $N_2$ are large (from about 30 upwards), a reasonably good estimate of the population variance is obtained by simply substituting the sample variance for it, so that we have

$$\text{standard error of difference} = \sqrt{s_1^2/N_1 + s_2^2/N_2}.$$

We can now use the expression for the standard error of the difference in order to find the probability of obtaining a difference of $(\bar{x}_1 - \bar{x}_2)$, or greater, under the null hypothesis. We do this by calculating a $z$-score based on the sampling distribution of the difference between means. We saw in chapter 5 that the ratio

$$z = \frac{\bar{x} - \mu}{\text{standard error}}$$

is normally distributed for large samples. In the present case, however, we are dealing not with single sample means but with differences between sample means. So we need to replace $\bar{x}$ (the sample mean) in the above expression by $(\bar{x}_1 - \bar{x}_2)$ (the difference between sample means), and $\mu$ (the population mean) by the difference between the means of the two populations. However, under the null hypothesis the populations have the same mean, so the difference between their means is zero. We also need to replace the standard error in the above expression by the standard error of the difference between means. We now have

$$z = \frac{(\bar{x}_1 - \bar{x}_2) - 0}{\text{standard error of difference}} = \frac{\bar{x}_1 - \bar{x}_2}{\sqrt{s_1^2/N_1 + s_2^2/N_2}}.$$

If we are operating with a significance level of $p \leqslant 0.05$, we know that the critical value of $z$ is 1.96 for a non-directional test, since this value cuts off 0.025 of the total area at each tail of the normal curve. For a directional test, the critical value of $z$ is 1.64, since this cuts off 0.05 of the area in a single tail, as shown in figure 7.1. If our calculated value of $z$ lies within the critical region (that is, exceeds the critical value of $z$), we may reject the null hypothesis at the 5 per cent level. Note that the sign of the calculated $z$ value depends only on which of the two means, $\bar{x}_1$ or $\bar{x}_2$, is larger.

Let us now consider an example of the application of the $z$-test. We calculated earlier the means and standard deviations of the two

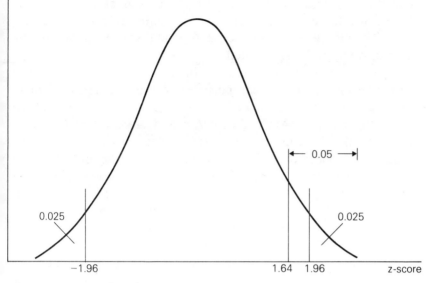

**Figure 7.1** Critical values of $z$ for $p \leqslant 0.05$ in a directional or non-directional test

sets of scores in our hypothetical experiment to test the effectiveness of two different methods of language teaching. The results were:

*Group A:* $\bar{x}_A = 14.93$ marks; $s_A = 2.49$ marks; $N_A = 30$.
*Group B:* $\bar{x}_B = 11.77$ marks; $s_B = 3.31$ marks; $N_B = 30$.

We shall set up the null hypothesis that there is no difference in the means of the populations from which the samples were drawn, and the alternative hypothesis that group A will have a higher mean score than group B (that is, a directional test with $\mu_A > \mu_B$). We shall use a significance level of $p \leqslant 0.01$.

Since the sample sizes are both 30, they just fulfil the requirement for a $z$-test. We proceed to calculate $z$ as follows:

$$z = \frac{\bar{x}_A - \bar{x}_B}{\sqrt{s_A^2/N_A + s_B^2/N_B}} = \frac{14.93 - 11.77}{\sqrt{(2.49)^2/30 + (3.31)^2/30}} = 4.18.$$

For a directional test with $p \leqslant 0.01$, we look up 0.01 in the body of the table of areas under the normal curve (table A2 of appendix 1) and find the critical value $z = 2.33$. Our calculated value is considerably bigger than this, and so lies within the critical region (indeed, the result would be significant even at the $p \leqslant 0.001$ level). We therefore reject the null hypothesis. Since $\bar{x}_A > \bar{x}_B$, the difference is in the predicted direction, so we can accept the alternative hypothesis as stated.

We shall now work through a further example, calculating $z$ from the raw data. For the purposes of this illustration, a small investigation into the mean word length of samples from two novels by Kingsley Amis, *Lucky Jim* and *Take a Girl Like You* (both in the Penguin edition) was carried out as follows. Ten pages were selected from each novel by the use of a random number table, and the first ten words on each selected page were taken, to give a random sample of 100 words from each novel. A word length distribution table was drawn up for each sample, taking hyphenated words and words with apostrophes as single items. The results are shown in table 7.1.

We wish to test the null hypothesis that the samples come from populations with the same mean. The alternative hypothesis is that the mean word lengths in the populations from which the samples are drawn (that is, in the two novels) are unequal: the test is therefore non-directional. We shall test for significance at the $p \leqslant 0.05$ level. The samples show a positively skewed rather than a normal distribution, but this will not invalidate the use of the $z$-test, since the samples are large.

First, we calculate the means and standard deviations:

$$\bar{x}_1 = \frac{\Sigma f x_1}{N_1} = \frac{415}{100} = 4.15 \text{ letters.}$$

$$s_1 = \sqrt{\frac{\Sigma f x_1^2 - (\Sigma f x_1)^2/N_1}{N_1 - 1}} = \sqrt{\frac{2\,255 - (415)^2/100}{99}}$$

$$= \sqrt{5.38} = 2.32 \text{ letters.}$$

$$\bar{x}_2 = \frac{\Sigma f x_2}{N_2} = \frac{434}{100} = 4.34 \text{ letters.}$$

$$s_2 = \sqrt{\frac{\Sigma f x_2^2 - (\Sigma f x_2)^2/N_2}{N_2 - 1}} = \sqrt{\frac{2402 - (434)^2/100}{99}}$$

$$= \sqrt{5.24} = 2.29 \text{ letters.}$$

**Table 7.1**  **Word length distribution in samples from two Kingsley Amis novels**

| Word length (letters) | Sample 1 (Lucky Jim) | Sample 2 (Take a Girl ... ) |
|:---:|:---:|:---:|
| 1 | 4 | 3 |
| 2 | 13 | 18 |
| 3 | 32 | 23 |
| 4 | 21 | 18 |
| 5 | 13 | 14 |
| 6 | 2 | 5 |
| 7 | 7 | 10 |
| 8 | 4 | 4 |
| 9 | 1 | 3 |
| 10 | | |
| 11 | 2 | |
| 12 | | 1 |
| 13 | | 1 |
| 14 | | |
| 15 | | |
| 16 | 1 | |
| | $N_1 = 100$ | $N_2 = 100$ |

We now calculate $z$ as follows:

$$z = \frac{\bar{x}_1 - \bar{x}_2}{\sqrt{s_1^2/N_1 + s_2^2/N_2}} = \frac{4.15 - 4.34}{\sqrt{(2.32)^2/100 + (2.29)^2/100}}$$
$$= -0.58.$$

The value of $z$, then, ignoring the sign, is 0.58. The critical value for $p \leqslant 0.05$ in a non-directional test is 1.96. Our calculated value is much smaller than this, and so lies outside the critical region. We cannot, therefore, reject the null hypothesis that the two samples come from populations with the same mean word length.

### 7.2.1.2   The t-test for small samples

We have seen that the $z$-test should be used only when the samples taken are large. When either or both of $N_1$ and $N_2$ fall below 30, the assumptions made in the $z$-test are no longer valid. In these circumstances, the ratio

$$\frac{\bar{x}_1 - \bar{x}_2}{\text{standard error of difference between means}}$$

is not normally distributed, but it does conform to the $t$ distribution, discussed in relation to estimation from small samples in section 5.4. We therefore use a $t$-test rather than a $z$-test whenever we are dealing with small samples.

The $t$-test makes two assumptions about the distributions of the populations from which the samples are drawn: that they are approximately normal, and that they have approximately equal variances. We have already discussed some simple ways of checking for approximate normality (see section 4.3); a further method will be outlined in chapter 9. Before going ahead with the $t$-test, a rough check should also be made to ensure that the variances are not too dissimilar; a more exact method of testing for equality of variance will be described in chapter 10. It has in fact been shown that the $t$-test is fairly 'robust', in that it is tolerant of all but rather large deviations from normality and equality of variance.

Let us now look at the rationale behind the $t$-test. Since the test assumes that the populations have the same variance, the best estimate of this common variance can be obtained by pooling the variability of the two samples. We do this by adding the sums of squares for the two samples, and dividing by the total number of degrees of freedom for both samples. If we call the pooled variance $s_p^2$, then

$$s_p^2 = \frac{\Sigma(x_1 - \bar{x}_1)^2 + \Sigma(x_2 - \bar{x}_2)^2}{(N_1 - 1) + (N_2 - 1)}$$

$$= \frac{\Sigma(x_1 - \bar{x}_1)^2 + \Sigma(x_2 - \bar{x}_2)^2}{N_1 + N_2 - 2}.$$

We know that the standard error of the difference between means is given by

$$\text{standard error of difference} = \sqrt{\sigma_1^2/N_1 + \sigma_2^2/N_2}.$$

Our estimate of the variance of each population is $s_p^2$, so we can write

$$\text{standard error of difference} = \sqrt{s_p^2/N_1 + s_p^2/N_2}$$
$$= \sqrt{s_p^2(1/N_1 + 1/N_2)}.$$

We can now write the expression for $t$ as follows:

$$t = \frac{\bar{x}_1 - \bar{x}_2}{\text{standard error of difference}} = \frac{\bar{x}_1 - \bar{x}_2}{\sqrt{s_p^2(1/N_1 + 1/N_2)}}$$

$$= \frac{\bar{x}_1 - \bar{x}_2}{\sqrt{\left(\dfrac{\Sigma(x_1 - \bar{x}_1)^2 + \Sigma(x_2 - \bar{x}_2)^2}{N_1 + N_2 - 2}\right)\left(\dfrac{1}{N_1} + \dfrac{1}{N_2}\right)}}.$$

This formula is inconvenient computationally, since it involves the subtraction of the mean from each observation. As with the formula for ordinary variances and standard deviations, we can rearrange as follows:

$$\Sigma(x_1 - \bar{x}_1)^2 = \Sigma x_1^2 - \frac{(\Sigma x_1)^2}{N_1}$$

$$\Sigma(x_2 - \bar{x}_2)^2 = \Sigma x_2^2 - \frac{(\Sigma x_2)^2}{N_2}.$$

An alternative expression for $t$, not involving subtraction of means, is therefore

$$t = \frac{\bar{x}_1 - \bar{x}_2}{\sqrt{\left(\dfrac{\Sigma x_1^2 - (\Sigma x_1)^2/N_1 + \Sigma x_2^2 - (\Sigma x_2)^2/N_2}{N_1 + N_2 - 2}\right)\left(\dfrac{1}{N_1} + \dfrac{1}{N_2}\right)}}.$$

Fearsome as this formula looks, it is quite easily handled if the calculation is performed in stages.

1   Calculate the means, $\bar{x}_1$ and $\bar{x}_2$; also calculate the variance estimate from the sums and sums of squares of the observed values, together with the sample sizes. The variances of the

individual samples should also be calculated, to check that they are roughly equal.

2   Use the variance estimate $(s_p^2)$ to calculate the standard error of the difference between means, using

$$\text{standard error of difference} = \sqrt{s_p^2(1/N_1 + 1/N_2)}.$$

3   Calculate $t$, using:

$$t = \frac{\bar{x}_1 - \bar{x}_2}{\text{standard error of difference}}.$$

We now look up, in table A3 of appendix 1, the critical value of $t$ for the chosen significance level, and for a directional or non-directional test, as appropriate. We can ignore the sign of $t$, since this simply depends on whether $\bar{x}_1 > \bar{x}_2$ or $\bar{x}_2 > \bar{x}_1$. It will be remembered from section 5.4 that the shape of the $t$-curve depends on the number of degrees of freedom involved, and that we therefore have to know this number in order to look up critical values of $t$. For our present situation, the total number of degrees of freedom is $(N_1 + N_2 - 2)$. If the calculated value of $t$ is greater than or equal to the critical value as determined from the table, we can reject the null hypothesis.

We shall now work through an example of the use of the $t$-test for small independent samples. The data in table 7.2 represent the number of sentences remembered correctly by two groups of

Table 7.2    Scores on a sentence recall test

| Group 1 (N₁ = 10) | Group 2 (N₂ = 9) |
|:---:|:---:|
| 18 | 13 |
| 15 | 14 |
| 13 | 12 |
| 17 | 6 |
| 14 | 11 |
| 8 | 13 |
| 10 | 17 |
| 11 | 16 |
| 7 | 5 |
| 17 | |

subjects, tested under two different conditions. The groups, one of 10 and one of 9 subjects, were constituted by random allocation of the 19 subjects. We wish to test the null hypothesis that the mean number of sentences recalled correctly is the same under the two conditions, at the $p \leqslant 0.05$ level, the alternative hypothesis being that the means of the populations from which the scores are drawn do differ.

We first calculate $\Sigma x$, $\Sigma x^2$ and $\bar{x}$ for each group:

$$\Sigma x_1 = 130 \qquad \Sigma x_2 = 107$$

$$\Sigma x_1^2 = 1\,826 \qquad \Sigma x_2^2 = 1\,405$$

$$\bar{x}_1 = 13.00 \qquad \bar{x}_2 = 11.89$$

and we then check that the variances of the two samples are similar:

$$s_1^2 = \frac{\Sigma x_1^2 - (\Sigma x_1)^2/N_1}{N_1 - 1} = \frac{1\,826 - 130^2/10}{9} = 15.11$$

$$s_2^2 = \frac{\Sigma x_2^2 - (\Sigma x_2)^2/N_2}{N_2 - 1} = \frac{1\,405 - 107^2/9}{8} = 16.61.$$

The variances are indeed similar, so we go on to calculate the pooled variance estimate $s_p^2$:

$$s_p^2 = \frac{\Sigma x_1^2 - (\Sigma x_1)^2/N_1 + \Sigma x_2^2 - (\Sigma x_2)^2/N_2}{N_1 + N_2 - 2}$$

$$= \frac{1\,826 - 130^2/10 + 1\,405 - 107^2/9}{10 + 9 - 2} = 15.82.$$

As a useful check, we note that this estimate lies between the values for the variances of the individual samples, as we should expect. We now calculate the standard error of the difference:

$$\text{standard error of difference} = \sqrt{s_p^2(1/N_1 + 1/N_2)}$$

$$= \sqrt{15.82(\tfrac{1}{10} + \tfrac{1}{9})} = 1.83.$$

Finally, we substitute in the formula for $t$:

$$t = \frac{\bar{x}_1 - \bar{x}_2}{\text{standard error of the difference}}$$

$$= \frac{13.00 - 11.89}{1.83} = 0.61.$$

The number of degrees of freedom is $(N_1 + N_2 - 2)$, or 17. Since we did not predict the direction of the difference between the means, we need a non-directional test. Table A3 tells us that a value of 2.11 is needed in a non-directional test for significance at the $p \leqslant 0.05$ level. Since our calculated value is much smaller than this, we cannot reject the null hypothesis, and we conclude that we have been unable to show a significant effect of the experimental condition on the mean number of sentences recalled correctly.

### 7.2.2    *A t-test for correlated samples*

If each subject in the investigation has performed under both conditions of an experiment, or if pairs of subjects have been matched for particular characteristics, a different approach to $t$-testing is required.

Our data consist of a set of paired observations. Let us denote a pair by $x_1$ and $x_2$, and their difference by $d$:

$$d = x_1 - x_2.$$

Although, as we have seen, $x_1$ and $x_2$ themselves may be correlated, reflecting characteristics of the subject or matched pair of subjects, this effect should be cancelled out by taking the difference between the scores. It is further assumed that the differences are normally distributed in the population from which they are drawn. The mean difference, $\bar{d}$, will be

$$\bar{d} = \frac{\Sigma(x_1 - x_2)}{N} = \frac{\Sigma x_1}{N_1} - \frac{\Sigma x_2}{N_2} = \bar{x}_1 - \bar{x}_2$$

where $N$ is the number of pairs of observations. Thus, the mean difference is equal to the difference between the means. Under the null hypothesis, the two samples come from populations with the same mean, and $\bar{d}$ will therefore be zero. What we need to test, therefore, is whether $\bar{d}$ is significantly different from zero. The reasoning behind the derivation of an expression for $t$ is similar to that discussed earlier for the $t$-test as applied to independent samples, and for the $z$-test. For the independent samples case, we have

$$t = \frac{\text{difference in sample means} - \text{difference in population means}}{\text{standard error of difference}}$$

$$= \frac{(\bar{x}_1 - \bar{x}_2) - 0}{\text{standard error of difference}}.$$

For the case of correlated samples, where we are dealing with the mean difference of our sample of pairs, the corresponding expression is

$$t = \frac{\bar{d} \text{ in sample of pairs} - \bar{d} \text{ in population}}{\text{standard error of } \bar{d}}$$

$$= \frac{\bar{d} - 0}{\text{standard error of } \bar{d}} = \frac{\bar{d}}{\text{standard error of } \bar{d}}$$

Now, just as the standard error of a mean is given by

$$\text{standard error} = \frac{s}{\sqrt{N}}$$

so the standard error of $\bar{d}$ is given by

$$\text{standard error} = \frac{\text{standard deviation of } d}{\sqrt{N}}.$$

The standard deviation of $d$ is calculated in just the same way as that of individual scores:

$$\text{standard deviation of } d = \sqrt{\frac{\Sigma(d - \bar{d})^2}{N - 1}}.$$

It follows that the expression for the standard error of $\bar{d}$ is

$$\text{standard error} = \sqrt{\frac{\Sigma(d-\bar{d})^2}{N-1}}\bigg/\sqrt{N} = \sqrt{\frac{\Sigma(d-\bar{d})^2}{N(N-1)}}\,.$$

We can now express $t$ as

$$t = \frac{\bar{d}}{\sqrt{\dfrac{\Sigma(d-\bar{d})^2}{N(N-1)}}} \qquad \text{with } (N-1) \text{ degrees of freedom (df).}$$

This formula is inconvenient because of the subtraction of $\bar{d}$ from each $d$ value. A more convenient formula is obtained by rearranging $\Sigma(d-\bar{d})^2$ in the usual way:

$$\Sigma(d-\bar{d})^2 = \Sigma d^2 - \frac{(\Sigma d)^2}{N}$$

$$t = \frac{\bar{d}}{\sqrt{\dfrac{\Sigma d^2 - (\Sigma d)^2/N}{N(N-1)}}}\,.$$

Since $\bar{d} = \Sigma d/N$, we can rearrange this further to give an even more convenient expression:

$$t = \frac{\Sigma d/N}{\sqrt{\dfrac{\Sigma d^2 - (\Sigma d)^2/N}{N(N-1)}}} = \frac{\Sigma d/N}{\sqrt{\dfrac{N\Sigma d^2 - (\Sigma d)^2}{N^2(N-1)}}}$$

$$= \frac{\Sigma d/N}{\sqrt{\dfrac{N\Sigma d^2 - (\Sigma d)^2}{N-1}}\bigg/N} = \frac{\Sigma d}{\sqrt{\dfrac{N\Sigma d^2 - (\Sigma d)^2}{N-1}}}\,.$$

As usual, we look up the critical value of $t$ for a directional or non-directional test, and for the appropriate number of degrees of freedom. We reject the null hypothesis if the critical value for the chosen significance level is equalled or exceeded.

One important point about the calculation should be noted: since we are interested in the overall difference between the two

**Table 7.3   Lengths of a vowel in two environments**

| Subject no. | Environment 1 | Environment 2 |
|---|---|---|
| 1 | 22 | 26 |
| 2 | 18 | 22 |
| 3 | 26 | 27 |
| 4 | 17 | 15 |
| 5 | 19 | 24 |
| 6 | 23 | 27 |
| 7 | 15 | 17 |
| 8 | 16 | 20 |
| 9 | 19 | 17 |
| 10 | 25 | 30 |

samples, we must record the sign of $d$ consistently in each case, so that we can calculate $\Sigma d$ correctly.

Let us now consider an example. The data in table 7.3 show the lengths (in arbitrary units) of syllables containing a particular vowel in two different environments. Each of the ten subjects was asked to read two sentences, each containing the vowel in one environment, and a pair of lengths was thus obtained for each subject. The experimenter predicts greater mean length in environment 2 than in environment 1.

The first step is to calculate the difference, $d$, between the members of each pair, and also $d^2$, as shown in table 7.4. We now calculate $t$ as follows:

$$t = \frac{\Sigma d}{\sqrt{\dfrac{N\Sigma d^2 - (\Sigma d)^2}{N-1}}} = \frac{-25}{\sqrt{\dfrac{(10 \times 127) - (-25)^2}{10-1}}} = -2.95.$$

Looking up the critical value for $t$ with $(N-1) = 9$ degrees of freedom for a directional test, we find $t = 1.833$ for the 5 per cent level. Since, ignoring the sign, our calculated $t$ value exceeds this, we can reject the null hypothesis, and claim that the means are significantly different at the 5 per cent level. Since $t$ is negative, reflecting a negative value of $\Sigma d$, the lengths in environment 2 are indeed greater on average than those in environment 1, so that the result is in the predicted direction. The means are, in fact:

Table 7.4    **Differences and squares of differences for vowel
length data**

| Environment 1 (N = 10) | Environment 2 (N = 10) | d | $d^2$ |
|---|---|---|---|
| 22 | 26 | −4 | 16 |
| 18 | 22 | −4 | 16 |
| 26 | 27 | −1 | 1 |
| 17 | 15 | 2 | 4 |
| 19 | 24 | −5 | 25 |
| 23 | 27 | −4 | 16 |
| 15 | 17 | −2 | 4 |
| 16 | 20 | −4 | 16 |
| 19 | 17 | 2 | 4 |
| 25 | 30 | −5 | 25 |
| | | $d = −25$ | $d^2 = 127$ |

$$\bar{x}_1 = \frac{\Sigma x_1}{N_1} = \frac{200}{10} = 20.0$$

$$\bar{x}_2 = \frac{\Sigma x_2}{N_2} = \frac{225}{10} = 22.5.$$

### 7.2.3    Deciding which test to use: a summary

We have now discussed three tests for the significance of differences between means. The flowchart in figure 7.2 summarises the
steps to be taken in deciding which test to use in any given case.

## 7.3    Testing the significance of differences between two
proportions, for independent samples

We can use arguments parallel to those for the differences between
means to derive a test statistic for the significance of the difference between the proportions of items, in two independent
samples, having a particular property. For instance, we might take
random samples of auxiliary verbs from two English texts, and
find that in one sample 28 auxiliaries out of 100 (that is, 28 per
cent) were modal verbs, while in the other sample 34 out of 90

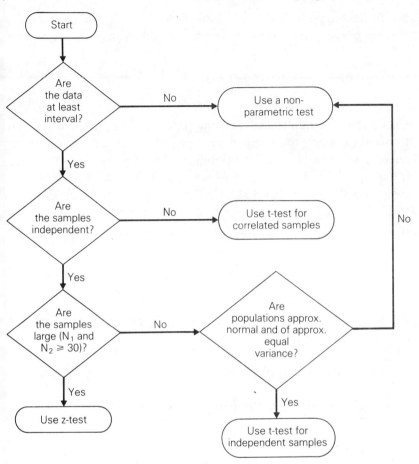

**Figure 7.2** Deciding which test of differences between means to use

(38 per cent) were modal. The question to be answered is whether this difference in the proportion of modals is significant, at some chosen significance level (say 1 per cent).

We saw in section 5.5 that the standard error of a proportion is given by

$$\text{standard error} = \sqrt{\frac{p(1-p)}{N}}$$

where

$p$ is the proportion of items having the property
$N$ is the sample size.

It can be shown that the standard error of the difference between two proportions $p_1$ and $p_2$, in samples of size $N_1$ and $N_2$, is given by

$$\text{standard error of difference} = \sqrt{\frac{p_1(1-p_1)}{N_1} + \frac{p_2(1-p_2)}{N_2}}.$$

Under the null hypothesis that the proportions in the two populations from which the samples are derived are equal, we can calculate a pooled estimate of the population parameter, and substitute it for $p_1$ and $p_2$ in the above expression. The best estimate of $p$ in the population, which we shall call $p_p$, is given by the ratio of the total frequency, in our samples, of the property we are interested in to the total size of the pooled samples; that is, by

$$p_p = \frac{f_1 + f_2}{N_1 + N_2}$$

where $f_1$ and $f_2$ are the frequencies of items with the required property. We now have

$$\text{standard error of difference} = \sqrt{p_p(1-p_p)\,(1/N_1 + 1/N_2)}.$$

We can now calculate a $z$-score as follows:

$$z = \frac{p_1 - p_2}{\text{standard error of difference}} = \frac{p_1 - p_2}{\sqrt{p_p(1-p_p)(1/N_1 + 1/N_2)}}.$$

Provided that $N_1$ and $N_2$ are reasonably large, and that $p_p$ is neither very small nor very large, $z$ is approximately normally distributed. In practice, as with estimation involving proportions (see section 5.5), we are safe if the product of $p_p$ or $(1-p_p)$ (whichever is smaller) and the smaller of $N_1$ and $N_2$ is at least 5. The critical value of $z$ is looked up in table A2, for the chosen significance level and for a directional or non-directional test, depending on whether or not the investigator has predicted which proportion will be the larger. If the $z$-score calculated for the data is greater than or equal to the critical value, we may reject the null hypothesis.

Let us apply this procedure to the problem of assessing the significance, at the 1 per cent level, of the difference in the proportions of modal verbs in two samples of auxiliaries, mentioned at the beginning of our discussion. We shall assume a non-directional alternative hypothesis, namely that the proportions in the populations concerned are unequal. We have

$$f_1 = 28 \qquad\qquad f_2 = 34$$

$$N_1 = 100 \qquad\qquad N_2 = 90$$

$$p_1 = 28/100 = 0.28 \qquad p_2 = 34/90 = 0.38$$

$$p_p = \frac{f_1 + f_2}{N_1 + N_2} = \frac{28 + 34}{100 + 90} = \frac{62}{190} = 0.33.$$

standard error of difference $= \sqrt{p_p(1 - p_p)(1/N_1 + 1/N_2)}$

$$= \sqrt{0.33(1 - 0.33)(\tfrac{1}{100} + \tfrac{1}{90})}$$

$$= 0.07.$$

$$z = \frac{p_1 - p_2}{\text{standard error of difference}} = \frac{0.28 - 0.38}{0.07}$$

$$= -1.43.$$

The value obtained is smaller than the critical value for the 1 per cent level in a non-directional test, which is 2.58. We therefore conclude that we are unable to demonstrate a significant difference in the proportions at the 1 per cent level. The result is also non-significant at the 5 per cent level, where the critical value is 1.96.

**Exercises**

1   For each of two texts, A and B, the number of different word types is measured in 50 samples of 500 word tokens (running words) each, with the following results:

*Text A*

| | | | | | | | | | |
|---|---|---|---|---|---|---|---|---|---|
| 307 | 372 | 297 | 280 | 291 | 320 | 344 | 312 | 303 | 311 |
| 262 | 316 | 341 | 317 | 331 | 378 | 301 | 361 | 270 | 336 |
| 282 | 278 | 298 | 268 | 350 | 327 | 235 | 314 | 260 | 291 |
| 309 | 242 | 343 | 284 | 311 | 288 | 329 | 368 | 307 | 338 |
| 253 | 309 | 380 | 322 | 352 | 391 | 290 | 373 | 258 | 250 |

*Text B*

| 310 | 288 | 333 | 385 | 344 | 348 | 321 | 363 | 340 | 380 |
| 274 | 352 | 335 | 373 | 401 | 270 | 292 | 366 | 388 | 346 |
| 312 | 326 | 301 | 342 | 382 | 349 | 355 | 338 | 375 | 408 |
| 281 | 296 | 368 | 392 | 346 | 352 | 330 | 306 | 342 | 383 |
| 318 | 357 | 339 | 378 | 412 | 351 | 298 | 370 | 398 | 418 |

(i)   Calculate the mean and the 99 per cent confidence limits for the mean, for each set of data.

(ii)  Test whether the means are significantly different at the 1 per cent level. You should provide full justification for the test you choose.

2   The following scores are obtained by two groups of subjects on a language proficiency test:

| Group A | Group B |
|---------|---------|
| 41 | 38 |
| 58 | 40 |
| 62 | 64 |
| 51 | 47 |
| 48 | 51 |
| 34 | 49 |
| 64 | 32 |
| 50 | 44 |
| 53 | 61 |
| 60 | |
| 44 | |

The investigator predicts that the means will differ significantly. Carry out a test to assess significance at the 5 per cent level, giving reasons for selecting the test you decide to use.

3   Each member of a group of ten subjects is asked to read two sentences, each containing a particular vowel segment, and the pitch level of the vowel is measured in each reading. The results (in arbitrary units) are as follows:

| Subject no. | Sentence 1 | Sentence 2 |
|-------------|------------|------------|
| 1 | 30 | 27 |
| 2 | 41 | 36 |
| 3 | 34 | 35 |
| 4 | 28 | 30 |

| 5 | 35 | 38 |
|---|----|----|
| 6 | 39 | 44 |
| 7 | 40 | 46 |
| 8 | 29 | 31 |
| 9 | 27 | 33 |
| 10 | 33 | 37 |

The experimenter predicts a higher mean pitch for the vowel in sentence 2. Carry out a *t*-test to assess significance at the 5 per cent level.

4   Twenty adult learners of Swahili are divided into two groups of ten at random. Group A is taught by a grammar–translation method, group B by an audio-lingual method. At the end of the course, the two groups obtain the following scores on a proficiency test:

| Group A | Group B |
|---------|---------|
| 45 | 48 |
| 58 | 58 |
| 60 | 71 |
| 51 | 56 |
| 53 | 59 |
| 59 | 62 |
| 54 | 64 |
| 40 | 62 |
| 56 | 52 |
| 56 | 69 |

It is predicted that group B will perform better, on average, than group A. Choose a statistical procedure that will test this prediction, discuss the reasons for your choice, and state any assumptions you are making. Then carry out the test and determine whether the differences are significant at the 5 per cent level.

5   Random samples of 100 sentences are taken from each of two texts, A and B. For sample A, 32 of the sentences are found to have lengths of 20 words or more, while for sample B the corresponding figure is 24 sentences. Test whether the proportions of long sentences are significantly different at the 1 per cent level.

# 8 Some useful non-parametric tests

## 8.1 Introduction

In this chapter, we examine three non-parametric tests which are useful in situations where the conditions for the parametric $z$- or $t$-tests are not met. These are the Mann–Whitney $U$-test, the Wilcoxon signed-ranks test and the sign test. As we shall see, each has a rather different range of applicability. A further non-parametric test, the chi-square test, is so important in linguistic statistics that the whole of chapter 9 will be devoted to it.

## 8.2 The Mann–Whitney $U$-test

The Mann–Whitney $U$-test is useful when we wish to know if two independent sets of data show a significant overall difference in the magnitude of the variable we are interested in, but we cannot use the $z$- or $t$-tests because the assumptions relating to level of measurement, sample size, normality or equality of variance are not valid. The test assumes only an ordinal level of measurement, since it is based on the ranking of scores. It is almost as powerful as the $t$-test, and so is a very useful alternative, especially as the test statistic is easy to calculate.

Under the null hypothesis, the two samples we are comparing come from populations with the same distribution. If we combine the samples and then assign ranks to each of the observations, allocating the rank 1 to the smallest, 2 to the next and so on, we shall expect, under the null hypothesis, that the scores from the two samples will be spread randomly in the rank ordering, so that the sum of ranks for each sample will be similar. If, on the other hand, there is a significant difference between the samples, we shall expect one sample to contribute values mainly to the upper part of the rank list, the other mainly to the lower part. The rank sums for the two samples will thus be considerably different. The Mann–Whitney $U$-test is used to calculate the probability of finding any given difference in rank sums under the null hypothesis that the samples were drawn from populations with the same distribution. As with other tests, the significance attached to the calculated value of the test statistic depends on the significance level chosen, and on whether the test is directional or non-directional.

We shall now consider how to calculate the test statistic $U$. Let the number of scores in the smaller group (if the groups are unequal in size) be $N_1$, and the number in the larger group $N_2$. Obviously, if the groups are equal in size, $N_1 = N_2$. We now rank the whole combined set of $N_1 + N_2$ scores from lowest (rank 1) to highest. If there is more than one occurrence of the same score (that is, 'tied' ranks), each occurrence is given the mean of the ranks which would have been allocated if there had not been a tie. For example, in the series 1, 2, 3, 3, 3, 5, the three occurrences of the score 3 would have occupied ranks 3, 4 and 5 if there had been no tie, and they are therefore each given the mean of these ranks (that is, 4). Since three ranks have been used, however, the next number (the 5 in our series) will have the rank of 6. We now obtain the sum of ranks $(R_1)$ for the smaller sample. If the samples are of equal size. either may be used. The value of $R_1$, together with those of $N_1$ and $N_2$, is substituted in the following expression for $U_1$:

$$U_1 = N_1 N_2 + \frac{N_1(N_1 + 1)}{2} - R_1.$$

We can now do the same for the larger group:

$$U_2 = N_1 N_2 + \frac{N_2(N_2 + 1)}{2} - R_2.$$

However, it can be shown, by rather tedious but fairly elementary algebra, that

$$U_2 = N_1 N_2 - U_1.$$

This formula is clearly more convenient for computation. We now take the smaller of $U_1$ and $U_2$, and call it $U$. The distribution of $U$ is known for various values of $N_1$ and $N_2$, and table A4 of appendix 1 gives the critical values for the 5 and 1 per cent levels in a non-directional test, or for the 2.5 and 0.5 per cent levels (that is, $p \leqslant 0.025$ and $p \leqslant 0.005$) in a directional test. The critical region contains $U$ values lying *below* the critical value, so that if our calculated value is *smaller* than or equal to the critical value we can reject the null hypothesis.

We shall now consider an example of the application of the Mann–Whitney test. Suppose that we have a group of 17 subjects for an investigation into the coherence of English texts. The subjects are allocated randomly to two groups, one of 9 and the other of 8 people. One group is given a short piece of text to read; the other group is given a different version of the text, in which various aspects of sentence linkage have been changed. The subjects are asked to grade the text they have read on a scale of coherence from 0 (totally incoherent) to 10 (totally coherent). The investigator wishes to know whether there is any significant difference between the two sets of ratings at the 5 per cent level in a non-directional test. The results are as shown in table 8.1.

We have two independent groups here, and an ordinal level of measurement, since we should not want to claim that coherence can be quantified in such a way that ratings of, say, 2 and 3 represent exactly the same amount of difference as ratings of 3 and 4, or 4 and 5, although we can say that a rating of 4 represents

**Table 8.1   Coherence ratings for two versions of a text**

| Original text (N₂ = 9) | Altered text (N₁ = 8) |
|:---:|:---:|
| 7 | 7 |
| 8 | 4 |
| 6 | 5 |
| 9 | 6 |
| 10 | 8 |
| 7 | 5 |
| 7 | 5 |
| 8 | 7 |
| 8 | |

greater coherence than one of 3, and so on. The conditions for a *t*-test do not, therefore, apply, but the non-parametric Mann–Whitney test can be used.

We first rank the combined scores, giving an average rank to tied scores, as in table 8.2. The rank sum for the smaller group ($R_1$) is 47. We can now use this value to find $U_1$:

$$U_1 = N_1 N_2 + \frac{N_1(N_1 + 1)}{2} - R_1$$

$$= (8 \times 9) + \frac{8(8 + 1)}{2} - 47 = 61.$$

Using the simpler formula for $U_2$, we have

$$U_2 = N_1 N_2 - U_1 = (8 \times 9) - 61 = 72 - 61 = 11.$$

Since $U_2$ is the smaller of the two values, we have $U = U_2 = 11$. Looking in table A4 for $N_1 = 8$ and $N_2 = 9$, we find that the critical value of $U$ for the 5 per cent level in a non-directional test is 15. Since our calculated value is less than this, we can reject the null hypothesis, and claim that there is a significant difference between the two sets of ratings.

Above values of about 20 for $N_1$ and $N_2$, the test statistic $U$ conforms to an approximately normal distribution. For large

**Table 8.2    Ranks for combined scores in coherence test**

| Original text | Rank | Altered text | Rank |
|---|---|---|---|
| 7 | 9 | 7 | 9 |
| 8 | 13.5 | 4 | 1 |
| 6 | 5.5 | 5 | 3 |
| 9 | 16 | 6 | 5.5 |
| 10 | 17 | 8 | 13.5 |
| 7 | 9 | 5 | 3 |
| 7 | 9 | 5 | 3 |
| 8 | 13.5 | 7 | 9 |
| 8 | 13.5 | | |
| | | | $R_1 = 47$ |

samples, then, we calculate a $z$ value as follows:

$$z = \frac{U - N_1 N_2/2}{\sqrt{\dfrac{N_1 N_2 (N_1 + N_2 + 1)}{12}}} \; .$$

If the calculated value of $z$ is greater than or equal to the critical value for the required significance level, as determined from table A2, we may reject the null hypothesis.

Let us suppose that we have calculated $U$ for two samples, one of 30 and one of 35 scores, and have obtained a value of 618. We calculate $z$ as follows:

$$z = \frac{618 - (30 \times 35)/2}{\sqrt{\dfrac{30 \times 35 \times (30 + 35 + 1)}{12}}} = 1.22.$$

If the test is non-directional and at the 5 per cent level, the critical value of $z$ is 1.96. Since the calculated value is smaller than this, we cannot reject the null hypothesis.

### 8.3    The Wilcoxon signed-ranks test

We saw above that the Mann–Whitney $U$-test can be used as a non-parametric counterpart of the $t$-test for independent samples, in conditions where the parametric test is inappropriate. The non-parametric equivalent of the $t$-test for correlated samples is the Wilcoxon signed-ranks test. This test assumes that we can rank differences between paired observations. Strictly speaking, then, it requires an interval level of measurement, since we need to be able to say that one difference is greater than another, and to calculate differences meaningfully the variable has to be measured in units of some kind. The test is a useful alternative to the $t$-test, however, since it is almost as powerful, and, being non-parametric, makes no assumptions about the shape of the distribution.

The data for the test will consist of a number of pairs of scores, each derived from a single subject, or from a pair of matched subjects. Under the null hypothesis that there is no difference in the distributions of the populations from which the samples are drawn, we should expect some of the differences between members of pairs to be positive and an approximately equal number to be negative. Furthermore, we should expect the sum of the positive differences to be roughly equal to the sum of the negative differences. If, on the other hand, the two sets of scores are representative of populations with different distributions, we should expect an imbalance in the numbers, and the sums, of positive and negative differences. The Wilcoxon signed-ranks test assesses the significance of the imbalance. The rationale of the test is thus very simple, and similar to that of the Mann–Whitney test for independent samples.

In order to calculate the test statistic, we first find the difference between each pair of scores, subtracting consistently (second from first, or vice versa) and recording the signs. We then rank the absolute values of the differences, ignoring the sign. If two scores in a pair are the same (that is, if the difference is zero), that pair is ignored altogether. If two values of the difference are tied, they are given the mean of the ranks they would have had if they had been different in value (compare the similar procedure in the Mann–Whitney test). Each rank is now given the sign of the difference it corresponds to. The sum of the positive ranks is found, and also that of the negative ranks. The smaller of these two sums is the test statistic $W$. Table A5 of appendix 1 gives the critical values of $W$ for the 5 and 1 per cent significance levels in a non-directional test, or for the 2.5 and 0.5 per cent levels in a directional test, for up to 25 pairs of scores. The value of $W$ must be *smaller* than or equal to the critical value if the null hypothesis is to be rejected. It should be noted that in taking an appropriate value for the number of pairs of scores $N$, pairs which are tied, and so have been discarded, are not counted.

As an example of the use of the Wilcoxon signed-ranks test, consider the situation where we tabulate the numbers of errors made by a group of 10 subjects in translating two passages of English, of equal length, into French. We wish to test, at the 5 per cent level, whether there is any significant difference between the two sets of scores. Since we are not predicting the direction of any such difference, a non-directional test will be appropriate. The scores observed are given in table 8.3.

We first calculate the differences, as shown in table 8.4, and rank them, giving a mean rank in the case of ties. We give each rank the sign of the difference it corresponds to. The pair with zero difference is dropped from the analysis, and $N$, the number

Table 8.3    **Errors made in translating two passages into French**

| Subject no. | Errors in passage A | Errors in passage B |
|:---:|:---:|:---:|
| 1 | 8 | 10 |
| 2 | 7 | 6 |
| 3 | 4 | 4 |
| 4 | 2 | 5 |
| 5 | 4 | 7 |
| 6 | 10 | 11 |
| 7 | 17 | 15 |
| 8 | 3 | 6 |
| 9 | 2 | 3 |
| 10 | 11 | 14 |

Table 8.4    Differences and ranks for translation error scores

| Passage A | Passage B | A − B | Rank |
|:---:|:---:|:---:|:---:|
| 8 | 10 | −2 | −4.5 |
| 7 | 6 | +1 | +2 |
| 4 | 4 | 0 | − |
| 2 | 5 | −3 | −7.5 |
| 4 | 7 | −3 | −7.5 |
| 10 | 11 | −1 | −2 |
| 17 | 15 | +2 | +4.5 |
| 3 | 6 | −3 | −7.5 |
| 2 | 3 | −1 | −2 |
| 11 | 14 | −3 | −7.5 |

of pairs, is decreased accordingly to 9. The sum of the positive ranks is 6.5, while that of the negative ranks is 38.5. We take the smaller of these, 6.5, as our value for $W$. From table A5, the critical value of $W$ for $N = 9$ and a 5 per cent significance level in a non-directional test is 5. Since our value of $W$ is larger than this, we cannot reject the null hypothesis, and must conclude that no significant difference has been demonstrated.

Where the number of pairs is greater than about 20, the distribution of $W$ is almost normal, and a $z$-score can be calculated from the computed $W$ value according to the following expression:

$$z = \frac{W - N(N+1)/4}{\sqrt{\dfrac{N(N+1)(2N+1)}{24}}}.$$

Let us consider the case where a value of $W = 209$ has been calculated for a set of data with $N = 35$. We then have

$$z = \frac{209 - (35 \times 36)/4}{\sqrt{\dfrac{35 \times 36 \times \{(2 \times 35) + 1\}}{24}}} = -1.74.$$

We can ignore the sign, which is normally negative. We know that values of $1.96$ and $1.64$ are required at the 5 per cent level for a non-directional or a directional test, respectively. Therefore if our test was non-directional we must conclude that no significant difference has been demonstrated. If, on the other hand, we had made a directional prediction, we could claim significance at the 5 per cent level.

## 8.4 The sign test

As we have seen, the Wilcoxon signed-ranks test requires a fairly high level of measurement. In many kinds of investigation of interest to the linguist, only an ordinal level can be achieved. Consider, for example, the case where informants are asked to rate two sentences on a scale of acceptability, or politeness, or some similar variable. Such variables (like coherence, discussed in relation to our example of the Mann–Whitney test in section 8.2) cannot really be measured in units with equal intervals, and we cannot attach much importance to the magnitude of differences between ratings; we could, however, claim that a sentence rated as, say, 4 on an acceptability scale had been rated as more acceptable than a sentence given a rating of 3. We can take into account the direction of the differences between pairs, even though we cannot use their magnitude. The loss of information incurred in ignoring the magnitude of the differences means that the so-called sign test, based on these principles, is less powerful than the Wilcoxon signed-ranks test, which does take the magnitude into account.

Under the null hypothesis that there is no difference in the distributions of the populations from which the samples are derived, we should expect, as we saw in discussing the Wilcoxon test, that the number of positive differences between the members of pairs of correlated scores would be roughly equal to the number of negative differences. The sign test computes the probability of obtaining any particular degree of deviation from this equality, under the null hypothesis. The situation is similar to that involved in the problem we looked at in section 1.2: calculating the probabilities of various combinations of males and females in a sample from a village with equal numbers of men and women. We saw that the so-called binomial distribution could be used to calculate these probabilities. Similarly, in the case of the sign test, we can compute the probability of obtaining 6 positive and 4 negative differences for 10 pairs, and so on.

To carry out the sign test, we first record the sign of the difference for each pair of scores, subtracting consistently. Tied scores are dropped from the analysis, and the number of pairs $(N)$ reduced accordingly. We now find the number of pairs with the *less* frequent sign, and call it $x$. Table A6 of appendix 1 gives critical values of $x$ for values of $N$ between 5 and 25, in a directional or non-directional test. If the computed value of $x$ is *smaller* than or equal to the critical value, we may reject the null hypothesis.

As an example of a situation where the sign test would be appropriate, let us consider the case where a group of subjects has been asked to rate a sentence on a scale of acceptability from 0 (totally unacceptable) to 5 (totally acceptable) for (a) informal spoken English and (b) formal written English. The investigator predicts that the sentence will be judged as more acceptable in informal spoken than in formal written English. The scores are given in table 8.5.

We first obtain the sign of each difference, and discount tied scores, as shown in table 8.6. We have 3 negative and 10 positive differences, so that $x = 3$ and $N = 13$. The critical value of $x$ at the 5 per cent level for $N = 13$ in a directional test is 3. Since the calculated value of $x$ is equal to the critical value, we can reject the null hypothesis at the 5 per cent level, and conclude that there

**Table 8.5    Acceptability ratings for a sentence in informal spoken and formal written English**

| Subject no. | Informal spoken | Formal written |
|:---:|:---:|:---:|
| 1 | 5 | 5 |
| 2 | 4 | 2 |
| 3 | 5 | 3 |
| 4 | 4 | 4 |
| 5 | 3 | 1 |
| 6 | 2 | 3 |
| 7 | 4 | 3 |
| 8 | 5 | 1 |
| 9 | 4 | 2 |
| 10 | 2 | 3 |
| 11 | 4 | 2 |
| 12 | 4 | 3 |
| 13 | 5 | 3 |
| 14 | 3 | 5 |
| 15 | 3 | 0 |

**Table 8.6    Sign of differences in acceptability scores**

| Informal spoken | Formal written | Sign of (informal − formal) |
|:---:|:---:|:---:|
| 5 | 5 | 0 |
| 4 | 2 | + |
| 5 | 3 | + |
| 4 | 4 | 0 |
| 3 | 1 | + |
| 2 | 3 | − |
| 4 | 3 | + |
| 5 | 1 | + |
| 4 | 2 | + |
| 2 | 3 | − |
| 4 | 2 | + |
| 4 | 3 | + |
| 5 | 3 | + |
| 3 | 5 | − |
| 3 | 0 | + |

is a significant difference between the two sets of scores, which is clearly in the predicted direction.

If $N$ is greater than about 25, it can be shown that an expression closely related to $x$ is normally distributed. We can calculate a $z$ value using the following expression, and refer it to the table of areas under the normal curve as usual:

$$z = \frac{N - 2x - 1}{\sqrt{N}}.$$

Let us imagine that we have 100 pairs of (non-tied) scores, and that 42 of the differences are positive and 58 negative. Then $x = 42$, and

$$z = \frac{100 - (2 \times 42) - 1}{\sqrt{100}} = 1.50.$$

This falls below the critical value for either a directional or a non-directional test at the 5 per cent level, so we should have to conclude that no significant difference between the two sets of scores had been demonstrated at this level.

## 8.5   Deciding which test to use: a summary

We conclude this chapter with a flowchart (figure 8.1) showing the steps to be taken in deciding which of the three tests discussed in this chapter should be used in a given case. For a much more detailed treatment of tests involving ranking, interested readers are referred to Meddis (1984).

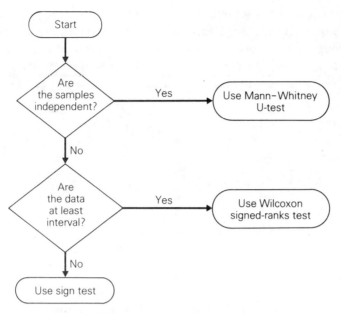

**Figure 8.1** Deciding which test to use

## Exercises

1 The following represent a teacher's assessments of reading skill for two groups of children:

| Group 1 | Group 2 |
|---------|---------|
| 8 | 4 |
| 6 | 6 |
| 3 | 3 |
| 5 | 3 |
| 8 | 7 |
| 7 | 7 |
| 7 | 5 |
| 6 | 5 |
| 5 | 4 |
| 6 | 4 |
| 6 | 6 |
| 7 | 5 |
| 8 | 6 |
|   | 5 |
|   | 4 |

Test, at the 2.5 per cent significance level, the hypothesis that the first group has a higher level of reading skill than the second.

2    Two sets of ten sentences, differing in their degree of syntactic complexity, are read individually, in randomised order, to a group of 30 informants, who are asked to repeat each sentence after a fixed time interval. The number of correctly remembered sentences in each set, for each informant, is as follows:

| Set 1 | Set 2 | Set 1 | Set 2 | Set 1 | Set 2 |
|-------|-------|-------|-------|-------|-------|
| 8 | 5 | 10 | 5 | 8 | 7 |
| 7 | 7 | 5 | 6 | 7 | 7 |
| 4 | 9 | 4 | 3 | 6 | 9 |
| 7 | 3 | 10 | 9 | 9 | 3 |
| 6 | 4 | 8 | 10 | 4 | 6 |
| 5 | 5 | 4 | 4 | 3 | 1 |
| 2 | 0 | 7 | 5 | 8 | 7 |
| 6 | 4 | 8 | 6 | 7 | 8 |
| 9 | 7 | 6 | 6 | 5 | 1 |
| 8 | 6 | 5 | 2 | 6 | 2 |

Using a non-parametric test, test the hypothesis that the two sets of scores differ significantly at the 5 per cent level.

3    An experiment is performed to test the effect of certain linguistic features on the politeness of two sentences in a particular social context. Fifteen informants are asked to rate the two sentences on a scale from 1 (very impolite) to 5 (very polite), with the following results:

| Informant no. | Sentence 1 | Sentence 2 |
|---------------|------------|------------|
| 1 | 1 | 3 |
| 2 | 2 | 2 |
| 3 | 1 | 4 |
| 4 | 2 | 3 |
| 5 | 3 | 1 |
| 6 | 2 | 4 |
| 7 | 1 | 1 |
| 8 | 2 | 3 |
| 9 | 3 | 5 |
| 10 | 1 | 3 |
| 11 | 2 | 3 |
| 12 | 1 | 4 |
| 13 | 2 | 1 |
| 14 | 2 | 4 |
| 15 | 1 | 3 |

Test the hypothesis that sentence 2 is rated as more polite than sentence 1, at the 5 per cent level.

4  Two comparable groups of children, whose native language is not English, are taught to read English by two different methods, and their reading fluency is then assessed on a scale from 1 to 10. The scores are as follows:

*Method A*  
6 4 8 3 4 5 5 6  
4 4 7 6 6 2 3

*Method B*  
5 5 8 9 7 5 6 7  
8 3 3 7 8 6 7

Do the two methods give signficantly different results at the 5 per cent level?

# 9 The chi-square test

## 9.1 Introduction

So far, we have discussed tests which will allow us to assess the significance of differences between two sets of quantitative measures on some particular variable, with a ratio, interval or ordinal level of measurement. In linguistics, however, we are often interested in comparing the frequencies, in two or more samples or populations, of characteristics that cannot be measured in units, but are of a yes-or-no type: that is, they are nominal variables. For instance, assuming that we can decide on clear-cut criteria, we can classify finite verbs in English as present or past in form, words as being either nouns or not nouns, and so on. We cannot score a verb for its 'degree of presentness', in the way that we can score, for example, a student's performance in a language test, or even the degree of acceptability of a sentence in a given context. We can, however, count the frequency of present-tense verbs, or of nouns, or the word *and*, in a text, and we may wish to compare this with the frequency in one or more other texts. In such cases, the non-parametric test known as the chi-square test is especially useful. 'Chi-square' is often written $\chi^2$, since $\chi$ is the Greek letter 'chi'. This test has probably been used more than any other in the study of linguistic phenomena.

## 9.2 General characteristics of the chi-square test

The chi-square test enables us to compare the frequencies we actually observe with those that we should expect on the basis of some theoretical model, or of a hypothesis about the distribution of the characteristics concerned. For each pair of observed and expected values, we calculate

$$\chi^2 = \sum \frac{(O-E)^2}{E}$$

where

$O$ = observed frequency
$E$ = expected frequency.

It is important to remember that $\chi^2$ must be calculated using frequencies, and *not* using the proportions of items having the characteristic concerned. For instance, if we found that a text sample had 45 present-tense forms out of a total of 100 finite verbs, we should use the frequency (45) in the calculation of the test statistic, not the proportion of present-tense forms (0.45).

An alternative form of the expression for $\chi^2$, which is sometimes easier to compute, is easily derived:

$$\chi^2 = \sum \frac{(O-E)^2}{E} = \sum \frac{O^2+E^2-2OE}{E} = \sum \frac{O^2}{E} + \Sigma E - 2\Sigma O.$$

Now, both $\Sigma E$ and $\Sigma O$ are equal to the total number of observations, $N$, so that

$$\chi^2 = \sum \frac{O^2}{E} + N - 2N = \sum \frac{O^2}{E} - N.$$

The null hypothesis is that there is no difference in distribution between the observed and expected values. The alternative hypothesis is usually that there *is* such a difference; that is, chi-square tests are usually non-directional, though directional tests can be carried out if required, by halving the significance levels associated with the critical values of the statistic for a non-directional test. The shape of the $\chi^2$ distribution, like that of the $t$ distribution, depends on the number of degrees of freedom involved. We shall discuss below how to calculate the appropriate number of degrees of freedom. Critical values of $\chi^2$ for varying numbers of degrees of freedom and varying significance levels are given in table A7 of appendix 1. These values are for the more usual non-directional type of test. If the calculated value of $\chi^2$ is greater than or equal to the critical value, the null hypothesis may be rejected.

### 9.3   Applications: goodness of fit

One important application of the chi-square test is in cases where we wish to check the degree to which a mathematical model or theoretical distribution fits a set of observed data. As an example, let us consider how to test whether a set of observed values could reasonably have been drawn from a population conforming to the normal distribution. Some very approximate tests for normality were discussed in section 4.3; the procedure to be considered here is a more precise test, suitable where we have a fairly large sample and wish to check on normality before, for instance, carrying out a $t$-test.

Let us suppose that we have asked 100 people to read a sentence containing a vowel in a particular phonological environment, and have measured the length of the vowel in each reading, with the results given as a frequency distribution in table 9.1. The mean and standard deviation, calculated by the usual methods, are 20.06 and 4.08 units, respectively. Our procedure will be to group the data into ten classes, each with an interval of two time units, and to calculate how many of our 100 observations we should expect to fall into each class, on the assumption that the distribution is

**Table 9.1   Vowel lengths in a particular environment**

| Length (0.01 sec) | Frequency | Length (0.01 sec) | Frequency |
|---|---|---|---|
| 10 | 1 | 21 | 10 |
| 11 | 1 | 22 | 8 |
| 12 | 2 | 23 | 7 |
| 13 | 2 | 24 | 5 |
| 14 | 3 | 25 | 6 |
| 15 | 4 | 26 | 3 |
| 16 | 6 | 27 | 3 |
| 17 | 6 | 28 | 1 |
| 18 | 9 | 29 | 1 |
| 19 | 10 | 30 | 1 |
| 20 | 11 | | |
| | | | $N = 100$ |

normal. We can then compare the observed and expected frequencies in each class by means of the chi-square test.

The grouped data are presented in the column labelled '*O*' in table 9.2 (the bracketing of the first three and last three values will be explained later). In order to calculate the expected frequencies in each class, we first determine the exact upper limits of the classes. It will be remembered that an interval of 10-11 really takes in all values greater than 9.50 but smaller than 11.50, and so on; the exact upper limits are shown in table 9.2.

The next step is to express each boundary in terms of its $z$-score equivalent, which tells us how many standard deviations away from the mean the boundary is. For instance, for the boundary at 11.50, we have

$$z = \frac{\text{boundary} - \text{mean}}{\text{standard deviation}} = \frac{11.50 - 20.06}{4.08} = -2.10.$$

From these $z$-scores, we wish to determine the proportion of observations expected to fall *below* each boundary, as a step on the way to calculating the proportions (and then the frequencies) *between* successive boundaries. Since, as determined from table A2, a $z$-score of $-2.10$ cuts off a tail of 0.018 of the total area, on the negative side of the normal curve, we know that 0.018 of the observations should be below the 11.50 boundary, and similarly for all the other negative values of $z$. When the sign of $z$ changes, we need to think carefully about what the values mean. For example, the $z$-score of 0.35 for the 21.50 boundary corresponds to a value of 0.363 of the area of the curve, as determined from table A2. But this means that 0.363 of the area is cut off in the positive tail of the curve, as shown in figure 9.1. Therefore the area lying below the $z$-score of 0.35 is $(1 - 0.363)$, or 0.637 of the total. Similarly, the $z$-score of 0.84 corresponding to the 23.50 boundary gives a tail, on the positive side, of 0.200 of the total area, so that $(1 - 0.200)$, or 0.800, of the observations should lie below the 23.50 boundary; and so on.

Now that we know the proportions of our observations expected to fall *below* each boundary, we can calculate those *between* boundaries by subtraction. For instance, since 0.018 of the observations should lie below the 11.50 boundary, and 0.054 below the 13.50 boundary, the proportion expected to be between 11.50 and 13.50 is $(0.054 - 0.018)$, or 0.036. Note that, since 0.990 of

**Table 9.2   Calculation of expected frequencies and computation of $\chi^2$ for vowel length data**

| Class interval | O | Upper limit | Deviation from $\bar{x}$ | $z = \dfrac{\text{deviation}}{s}$ | Proportion below | Proportion within | E | $\dfrac{(O-E)^2}{E}$ |
|---|---|---|---|---|---|---|---|---|
| 10-11 | 2 ⎫ 13 | 11.50 | −8.56 | −2.10 | 0.018 | 0.018 | 1.8 ⎫ | |
| 12-13 | 4 ⎬ | 13.50 | −6.56 | −1.61 | 0.054 | 0.036 | 3.6 ⎬ 13.1 | 0.00 |
| 14-15 | 7 ⎭ | 15.50 | −4.56 | −1.12 | 0.131 | 0.077 | 7.7 ⎭ | |
| 16-17 | 12 | 17.50 | −2.56 | −0.63 | 0.264 | 0.133 | 13.3 | 0.13 |
| 18-19 | 19 | 19.50 | −0.56 | −0.14 | 0.444 | 0.180 | 18.0 | 0.06 |
| 20-21 | 21 | 21.50 | 1.44 | 0.35 | 0.637 | 0.193 | 19.3 | 0.15 |
| 22-23 | 15 | 23.50 | 3.44 | 0.84 | 0.800 | 0.163 | 16.3 | 0.10 |
| 24-25 | 11 | 25.50 | 5.44 | 1.33 | 0.908 | 0.108 | 10.8 | 0.00 |
| 26-27 | 6 ⎫ 9 | 27.50 | 7.44 | 1.82 | 0.966 | 0.058 | 5.8 ⎫ | |
| 28-29 | 2 ⎬ | 29.50 | 9.44 | 2.31 | 0.990 | 0.024 | 2.4 ⎬ 9.2 | 0.00 |
| >29 | 1 ⎭ | | | | | 0.010 | 1.0 ⎭ | |
| | | | | | | 1.000 | 100.0 | 0.44 |

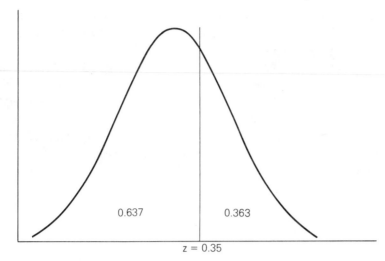

0.637    0.363

z = 0.35

**Figure 9.1**    Interpretation of the positive values of $z$

the observations are expected to be below the 29.50 boundary, $(1-0.990)$, or $0.010$, should be above it.

We now calculate the expected *frequencies* in each class by multiplying the expected proportions by the total sample size, that is 100. The results are as shown in the column headed '$E$' in table 9.2: they total to 100, as of course they should.

The contribution of each pair of observed and expected frequencies to the value of $\chi^2$ can now be calculated by computing $(O-E)^2/E$ for each pair. There is, however, one important point to bear in mind here. The $\chi^2$ test has been shown to be unreliable when any of the expected frequencies falls below about 5. For this reason, we may have to combine frequencies (where it is sensible to do so) until the combined classes have an expected frequency of 5 or more. This is why the frequency values for the first three classes, and also those for the last three, have been combined as shown in table 9.2.

The sum of all the $(O-E)^2/E$ values is, of course, the value of the test statistic $\chi^2$, which in the present case is 0.44. There remains the problem of deciding how many degrees of freedom are involved. Taking into account the combination of classes, discussed above, we have used seven pairs of $E$ and $O$ values in the calculation of $\chi^2$. But the distributions of observed and expected frequencies have been made to agree on three values: those of the sample size, the mean and the standard deviation. That is, these three values are not free to vary between the two distributions, and so we have not 7, but $(7-3)$, or 4, degrees of freedom. Looking in table A7, we find that the critical value of $\chi^2$ for 4 degrees of freedom is 9.49 at the 5 per cent level. Our calculated value is very far below this, so that we cannot reject the null hypothesis that the observed and expected values have the same distribution. (In fact, there is about a 98 per cent chance of obtaining the observed differences or less under the null hypothesis.) We therefore conclude that the observed set of data conforms very closely to the normal distribution (or, more precisely, that the probability of non-normality is extremely low).

Procedures such as this are extremely useful in testing mathematical models of linguistic phenomena. For instance, much effort has been put into the attempt to find mathematical expressions which will describe the frequency profile of lexical items in a text (the number of words occurring once, twice, three times, and so on). The chi-square test would be an appropriate way of assessing the significance of discrepancies between the observed frequencies and those predicted by the model.

### 9.4    Applications: tests of independence and association

A second, and very common, application of the chi-square test is to situations where we wish to test whether two characteristics are independent, or are associated in such a way that high frequencies of one tend to be coupled with high frequencies of the other.

Let us imagine that we are investigating the relationship between tense and aspect in a particular language, and have classified the verbal phrases in a set of texts as being either present or past tense (we shall ignore any other distinctions), and also as either progressive or non-progressive in aspect. We can now arrange our data in the form of a $2 \times 2$ table, normally called a 'contingency table', as shown in table 9.3.

On the null hypothesis, there is no association between the two features, past/present and progressive/non-progressive. This means that we can calculate the expected frequency in each 'cell' of the table, under the null hypothesis. We know that $784/1\,396$ of the total sample of verbal phrases are progressive. If there is no connection between aspect and tense, the same proportion of the past

**Table 9.3  Classification of verb phrases for tense and aspect**

| Aspect | Past tense | Present tense | Total |
|---|---|---|---|
| Progressive | 308 | 476 | 784 |
| Non-progressive | 315 | 297 | 612 |
| Total | 623 | 773 | 1 396 |

**Table 9.4  Expected frequencies of tense and aspect categories under the null hypothesis**

| Aspect | Past tense | Present tense | Total |
|---|---|---|---|
| Progressive | 349.9 | 434.1 | 784 |
| Non-progressive | 273.1 | 338.9 | 612 |
| Total | 623 | 773 | 1 396 |

verb phrases should be progressive. Since the total number of past phrases is 623, the expected number of phrases with both past and progressive features is

$$E = \frac{784}{1\,396} \times 623 = 349.9.$$

We could go on in the same way to calculate the expected frequencies in the other three cells of the table. Note, however, that since there are 623 past phrases in all, and 349.9 of these are predicted to be progressive, the number of non-progressive phrases is expected to be $(623 - 349.9)$, or 273.1. We can calculate the other two values in the same way. This demonstrates one important characteristic of a $2 \times 2$ table: since, if we know one cell value and the marginal totals, we can calculate the other three cell values, there is only one value that is free to vary, and therefore only one degree of freedom. The expected frequencies are given in table 9.4. In practice, these values are often written in brackets, beside the observed values, in the same table.

We now calculate $\chi^2$ as follows:

$$\chi^2 = \frac{(308 - 349.9)^2}{349.9} + \frac{(315 - 273.1)^2}{273.1} + \frac{(476 - 434.1)^2}{434.1}$$

$$+ \frac{(297 - 338.9)^2}{338.9}$$

$$= 5.02 + 6.43 + 4.04 + 5.18 = 20.67.$$

Referring to table A7, we find that the critical value for the 5 per cent level and one degree of freedom is 3.84. Since our value of $\chi^2$ is much greater than this, we conclude that the null hypothesis can be rejected at this level (indeed, the value obtained is significant even at the 0.1 per cent level). There is thus a significant association between tense and aspect. Inspection of the contingency tables shows that there is a positive association between present tense and progressive aspect, and between past tense and non-progressive aspect. We could, if we wished, confirm this by testing the significance of the difference between the proportions of progressive and non-progressive phrases for one of the tenses (see section 7.3). This is left as an exercise for the reader.

For the case of a $2 \times 2$ table, as above, there is a formula that is computationally more convenient than the calculation of $\chi^2$ from first principles. If we have a table of observed values with entries as follows:

| | | |
|---|---|---|
| $A$ | $B$ | $A + B$ |
| $C$ | $D$ | $C + D$ |

$A + C \quad B + D \quad$ Grand total $= A + B + C + D$

then

$$\chi^2 = \frac{N(AD - BC)^2}{(A + B)(C + D)(A + C)(B + D)}.$$

For the tense and aspect data discussed earlier, we have

$$\chi^2 = \frac{1\,396\{(308 \times 297) - (476 \times 315)\}^2}{784 \times 612 \times 623 \times 773} = 20.65.$$

The very slight discrepancy in the values of $\chi^2$ obtained by the two methods is due to rounding errors in the computation of expected values in the first method.

We can extend the general argument for the chi-square test to cover cases with a larger number of intersecting features, though the quick method of computation will no longer be available. Let us suppose that we have categorised all the sentences in samples from three novels as 'long' (more than 25 words), 'medium' (10–25 words) or 'short' (fewer than 10 words), and have found the frequencies shown in table 9.5. The expected frequencies are found by exactly the same kind of reasoning as for the 2 × 2 table, and can in fact be calculated for each cell as follows:

$$E = \frac{\text{row total} \times \text{column total}}{\text{grand total}}.$$

Thus the expected value for short sentences in novel 1 is

$$E = \frac{295 \times 500}{1\,499} = 98.4.$$

The expected frequencies (those predicted under the null hypothesis of no association between sentence length and novel) are written in brackets in table 9.5. We now proceed to calculate $\chi^2$ in the usual way, by summing the values of $(O - E)^2/E$. We obtain a value of 8.15 for our data. The number of degrees of freedom is determined by the fact that if we know all but one of the values in a row or column, and also the row or column total, the remaining cell entry can be worked out. Therefore

$$\text{degrees of freedom} = (\text{no. of rows} - 1) \times (\text{no. of columns} - 1).$$

**Table 9.5  Sentence lengths in three novels**

| Sentence length | Novel 1 | Novel 2 | Novel 3 | Total |
|---|---|---|---|---|
| Short | 103 (98.4) | 82 (96.2) | 110 (100.4) | 295 |
| Medium | 281 (273.2) | 262 (267.2) | 276 (278.6) | 819 |
| Long | 116 (128.4) | 145 (125.6) | 124 (131.0) | 385 |
| Total | 500 | 489 | 510 | 1 499 |

Note that the $2 \times 2$ table, with one degree of freedom, is simply a particular case of this relation, since $(2-1) \times (2-1) = 1$. For the $3 \times 3$ table we are dealing with at present, the number of degrees of freedom is $(3-1) \times (3-1) = 4$, and the critical value of $\chi^2$ at the 5 per cent level, as determined from table A7, is 9.49. Since the calculated value of $\chi^2$ is smaller than this, we cannot reject the null hypothesis at the 5 per cent level; in other words, we have failed to find significant evidence of association between sentence length and novel.

We saw earlier that the chi-square test is unreliable when the expected frequency in any cell falls below 5. The effects of small frequencies are particularly important in the case of $2 \times 2$ contingency tables. One of the assumptions behind the test, namely that the values correspond to a continuous rather than a discrete frequency distribution, is not valid under these circumstances, and it is advisable to apply a 'continuity correction', often called Yates's correction. The formula for $\chi^2$ is modified as follows:

$$\chi^2 = \sum \frac{(|O-E|-\frac{1}{2})^2}{E}$$

where $|O-E|$ is the 'absolute' value of the difference between $O$ and $E$, ignoring the sign. It is best to apply this correction whenever there are fairly small numbers in any cells of a $2 \times 2$ table; with larger frequencies the effect of the correction is small. The formula given earlier for the direct calculation of $\chi^2$ for a $2 \times 2$ table is modified as follows:

$$\chi^2 = \frac{N(|AD-BC|-\frac{1}{2}N)^2}{(A+B)(C+D)(A+C)(B+D)} .$$

As an example of the use of Yates's correction, consider the hypothetical data in table 9.6 on the use of a monophthongal or a diphthongal pronunciation of the vowel in a particular word, by Liverpool speakers born before or after 1940. Applying the direct formula given above, we have

$$\chi^2 = \frac{25 \times \{|(6 \times 2) - (8 \times 9)| - \frac{25}{2}\}^2}{14 \times 11 \times 15 \times 10}$$

$$= \frac{25 \times (|12-72| - 12.5)^2}{23\,100}$$

Table 9.6  Pronunciation of a vowel by Liverpool speakers

| Vowel | Born before 1940 | Born 1940 or later | Total |
|---|---|---|---|
| Monophthong | 6 (8.4) | 8 (5.6) | 14 |
| Diphthong | 9 (6.6) | 2 (4.4) | 11 |
| Total | 15 | 10 | 25 |

$$= \frac{25 \times (60 - 12.5)^2}{23\,100} = 2.44.$$

If our test is at the 5 per cent level, the critical value of $\chi^2$ for one degree of freedom is 3.84. We therefore conclude that there is insufficient evidence to claim any interaction between age and vowel pronunciation in this case, despite the apparent association shown in the contingency table.

**Exercises**

1   In the author's study of the poetry of Sylvia Plath (Butler, 1979) the word length distributions for two books of poetry were found to be as follows:

| Word length (letters): | 1–3 | 4–6 | 7–9 | 10–12 | >12 |
|---|---|---|---|---|---|
| Frequency in | | | | | |
| *The Colossus*: | 3 473 | 3 743 | 1 272 | 285 | 54 |
| *Winter Trees*: | 3 000 | 2 674 | 753 | 165 | 18 |

Use the chi-square test to decide whether the word length distributions differ significantly at the 5 per cent level.

2   In the same investigation of Plath's poetry, the following frequencies were found, in the four collections of poems studied, for items containing *black*:

| *The Colossus* | *Crossing the Water* | *Ariel* | *Winter Trees* |
|---|---|---|---|
| 27 | 28 | 46 | 26 |

The total number of running words in each collection of poems is: *The Colossus*, 8 827; *Crossing the Water*, 7 949; *Ariel*, 9 340; *Winter Trees*, 6 610. Test whether the use of *black* is evenly distributed over the four books of poems, using a 5 per cent significance level.

3   Again in the Plath study, the frequencies of certain punctuation marks in the four collections were examined, with the results shown in table 9.7. By applying the chi-square test to each punctuation mark in turn, assess the significance of this aspect of the poet's style, assuming that the punctuation of the text has not been altered by editorial revisions. Assume also that the expected frequency of a given punctuation mark in each text is proportional to the length of the text (for text lengths, see question 2 above).

**Table 9.7**

|  | The Colossus | Crossing the Water | Ariel | Winter Trees |
|---|---|---|---|---|
| Full stop | 536 | 545 | 660 | 524 |
| Comma | 749 | 581 | 885 | 608 |
| Colon | 65 | 41 | 24 | 15 |
| Semi-colon | 25 | 19 | 16 | 6 |
| Exclamation mark | 17 | 34 | 29 | 54 |
| Question mark | 5 | 16 | 77 | 53 |
| Dash | 30 | 52 | 77 | 51 |

4   Sentence length distributions in the Plath poetry were also studied, with the results shown in table 9.8. Use the chi-square test to examine the sentence length distribution in the texts, and comment on your findings.

**Table 9.8**

| Sentence length (no. words) | The Colossus | Crossing the Water | Ariel | Winter Trees |
|---|---|---|---|---|
| 1–5 | 90 | 85 | 141 | 191 |
| 6–10 | 159 | 218 | 277 | 229 |
| 11–15 | 113 | 113 | 170 | 94 |
| 16–20 | 66 | 72 | 71 | 57 |
| 21–25 | 42 | 50 | 44 | 24 |
| 26–30 | 19 | 26 | 23 | 14 |
| 31–35 | 19 | 15 | 18 | 10 |
| 36–40 | 21 | 9 | 11 | 8 |
| >40 | 29 | 9 | 12 | 6 |

5   In question 2 of the chapter 2 exercises were given the intensities of 100 stressed and 100 unstressed syllables in a sample of spoken French. Using the chi-square test as a test of goodness of fit, determine whether each set of observations departs significantly from the normal distribution at the 5 per cent level.

6   Coates and Leech (1980), in a study of the distribution of various meanings of the modal verbs in British and American English, found the following distributions for 'root' and 'epistemic' meanings of *must* and *have to* in their corpus:

|            | British | American |
|------------|---------|----------|
| *must*     |         |          |
| root       | 153     | 150      |
| epistemic  | 74      | 47       |
| *have to*  |         |          |
| root       | 226     | 209      |
| epistemic  | 2       | 9        |

Calculate a value for $\chi^2$ in each case, and interpret the findings.

7   Connolly (1979), studying syntactic change in Middle English, examined the frequencies of certain clause structure patterns in three early and three late Middle English (ME) texts.

(i)   His results on the frequency of contiguity of predicator and a following major element of structure in declarative affirmative clauses are shown below:

|          | Non-contiguous | Contiguous |
|----------|----------------|------------|
| Early ME |                |            |
| Text 1   | 29             | 129        |
| Text 2   | 29             | 168        |
| Text 3   | 17             | 158        |
| Late ME  |                |            |
| Text 1   | 14             | 159        |
| Text 2   | 29             | 180        |
| Text 3   | 23             | 195        |

Calculate a $\chi^2$ value for the variation between the texts in each group taken separately. Then pool the frequencies for the three texts in each group, and perform a second chi-square test to assess differences in the pattern of contiguity between the groups. What do the results tell you?

(ii)  Connolly also studied the contiguity of subject and predicator in the two groups of texts, with the following results:

|  | Non-contiguous | Contiguous |
|---|---|---|
| **Early ME** | | |
| Text 1 | 16 | 124 |
| Text 2 | 27 | 155 |
| Text 3 | 9 | 149 |
| **Late ME** | | |
| Text 1 | 4 | 179 |
| Text 2 | 10 | 201 |
| Text 3 | 5 | 203 |

Calculate $\chi^2$ values for the variation within each group, and interpret your findings.

(iii)  A third study involved the frequency of inversion of subject and verb after an introductory adverbial in declarative affirmative clauses:

|  | No inversion | Inversion |
|---|---|---|
| **Early ME** | | |
| Text 1 | 27 | 11 |
| Text 2 | 34 | 16 |
| Text 3 | 34 | 14 |
| **Late ME** | | |
| Text 1 | 109 | 27 |
| Text 2 | 61 | 11 |
| Text 3 | 49 | 29 |

Calculate $\chi^2$ values for the variation within each group, and interpret the results.

# 10 The $F$ distribution and its uses

## 10.1 Introduction

In section 5.2 we discussed the sampling distribution of the means of samples taken from the same population, and in section 7.2 we extended the concept of sampling distribution to the difference between the means of pairs of samples from a population. In the present chapter we consider a further sampling distribution, concerned with the variances of samples from a population.

Consider the case where we take samples, of sizes $N_1$ and $N_2$ respectively, from either a single population or two populations with the same variance. We calculate the variances for both samples ($s_1^2$ and $s_2^2$) and then find the ratio $s_1^2/s_2^2$. If we did this for a very large number of pairs of samples, the ratios would form a distribution known as the $F$ distribution, whose properties are known for various numbers of degrees of freedom, these being $(N_1 - 1)$ and $(N_2 - 1)$ for the two samples. In other words, tables of $F$, the ratio of $s_1^2$ to $s_2^2$, allow us to find the probability of obtaining $F$ ratios above any given value, for two samples from the same population, or from two populations with the same variance. Table A8 of appendix 1 gives the critical values of $F$ which are equalled or exceeded with 5 or 1 per cent probability, for various combinations of degrees of freedom, in a directional or one-tailed test and in a non-directional or two-tailed test.

## 10.2 Testing for homogeneity of variance

There are occasions on which we may need to know whether or not the variances of two samples differ sufficiently for us to be able to reject the null hypothesis that the variances of the populations from which the two samples were drawn are equal. This is usually known as testing for 'homogeneity of variance'. We may be interested in variability for its own sake (see section 3.3.1), or we may wish to confirm that the assumption of homogeneity of variance made by a parametric test such as the *t*-test is a reasonable one.

To perform the test, we calculate the variance for each sample, and take the ratio of the larger to the smaller variance, so that the *F* value obtained is never less than 1. We then look up the critical value of *F* in table A8 for the required significance level. We look along the top of the table for the number of degrees of freedom $(N_1 - 1)$ associated with the larger variance, and then follow this column down until we find the row corresponding to the number of degrees of freedom $(N_2 - 1)$ associated with the smaller variance. The intersection of the appropriate column and row gives the required value of *F*. We must use a non-directional or two-tailed test since our decision to place the bigger variance in the numerator of the *F* ratio was purely arbitrary, and we have not in fact predicted which variance will be the greater. The critical values given in table A8 therefore correspond to the 10 and 2 per cent levels in this test. If the calculated value equals or exceeds the critical value for a particular significance level, we must reject the null hypothesis and conclude that the variances are significantly different. Otherwise, we may safely assume that we have no good evidence to abandon the claim of homogeneity of variance.

In section 7.2.1.2 we performed a *t*-test to assess the significance of the difference in means between two independent sets of scores on a sentence recall test. We calculated the variances and found that they did indeed seem quite similar. Let us now show that we were correct in assuming homogeneity of variance in this case. The variances were as follows:

$$s_1^2 = 15.11 \text{ for } N = 10$$
$$s_2^2 = 16.61 \text{ for } N = 9.$$

Taking *F* as the ratio of the larger to the smaller variance, we have

$$F = \frac{16.61}{15.11} = 1.10.$$

There are $(9 - 1)$ or 8 degrees of freedom for the calculation of the larger variance, and $(10 - 1)$ or 9 degrees of freedom for the smaller variance. We now look in table A8, finding the column corresponding to the degrees of freedom for the larger variance, and the row corresponding to the degrees of freedom for the smaller variance. The critical value is 3.23 at the 10 per cent level and 5.47 at the 2 per cent level (remembering that we are dealing here with a non-directional test). Since our calculated value is much smaller than either of these critical values, we cannot reject the null hypothesis even at the 10 per cent level, and we can conclude that we are safe in assuming homogeneity of variance.

## 10.3 An introduction to the analysis of variance (ANOVA) technique

The most common and useful application of the $F$-test is in the technique known as 'analysis of variance', often abbreviated to ANOVA. This is a very complex area, and we can do no more than give a brief introduction here.

In chapter 7 we discussed $z$- and $t$-tests for assessing the significance of the difference between the means for two independent samples. Sometimes, however, we may wish to compare the means of more than two independent samples. We could, of course, test each possible pairing by means of a $z$- or $t$-test, as appropriate. This could get very tedious, however, since with $N$ sets of data there are $N(N-1)/2$ pairs, so that if, for example, we had 6 sets of results, there would be $6 \times 5/2$ or 15 individual comparisons to make. By means of the analysis of variance technique, we can test whether there are any significant differences between the means overall, without having to test each pair separately. If there are significant differences, we can, of course, proceed to find out which pairs differ, using a $z$- or $t$-test.

We shall now discuss in very simple terms the rationale behind the ANOVA technique. Suppose that we have a number of sets of scores or frequencies for some linguistic variable. The overall variability in the whole collection of observations can be split into two parts. First, each group of observations will show some variation within itself, owing to sampling variability. There will also be variation between groups. We can calculate a variance estimate for the population based on each of these sources of variability. If all the observations come from the same population, or from populations with equal means and variances, we shall expect that the estimates based on within-groups variability and between-groups variability will be roughly equal, and therefore that their ratio will be approximately 1. But if the samples are from populations with different means, so that there is a source of variability other than just that arising from sampling, then we shall expect the between-groups variability to be considerably larger than the within-groups variability, so that the ratio $s^2_{\text{between}}/s^2_{\text{within}}$ will be greater than unity. We can use the $F$-test to determine whether the observed departure of the ratio from unity is significant at any chosen level.

Let us now consider in rather more detail the calculations involved in a simple application of the ANOVA method. Remember that what we are trying to do is partition the variation shown in the whole collection of data into two parts, corresponding to variability within and between groups. The variances associated with each of the two sources of variation are usually not themselves additive. We can see why if we remember that the expression for variance is

$$s^2 = \frac{\Sigma(x - \bar{x})^2}{N - 1}$$

so that the number of degrees of freedom, which will normally be different for the within-groups and between-groups estimates, is involved. The sums of squares of deviations from the mean are, however, additive, and it is these that we partition. If we call the total sum of squares $SS_t$, the within-groups sum of squares $SS_w$ and the between-groups sum of squares $SS_b$, then

$$SS_t = SS_w + SS_b.$$

The easiest way to proceed is to calculate $SS_t$ and $SS_b$, and then to obtain $SS_w$ by subtraction. The required series of steps is therefore as follows.

*Step 1*   Calculate $SS_t$, given by

$$SS_t = \Sigma(x - \bar{x})^2$$

where

$x$ = each observation
$\bar{x}$ = grand mean of all the observations.

It is, of course, usually much easier to use the alternative formula which does not involve subtracting the mean from each observation:

$$SS_t = \Sigma x^2 - \frac{(\Sigma x)^2}{N}.$$

*Step 2*  Calculate $SS_b$. This is, in fact, the sum of squares of the deviations of each individual group mean from the grand mean:

$$SS_b = \Sigma(\bar{x}_{group} - \bar{x}_{grand})^2.$$

Once again, however, there is a more convenient formula:

$$SS_b = \frac{(\Sigma x_1)^2}{N_1} + \frac{(\Sigma x_2)^2}{N_2} + \frac{(\Sigma x_3)^2}{N_3} + \ldots - \frac{(\Sigma x)^2}{N}$$

where the subscripts 1, 2, 3 and so on refer to the groups of observations. Thus, for each group we add up all the values, square the result and divide by the number of values. We then sum all the resulting figures, and finally subtract $(\Sigma x)^2/N$, as calculated for the whole collection of observations.

*Step 3*  Calculate $SS_w$. This is in fact the sum of squares of the deviation of each observation from the mean for the particular group to which it belongs. It can be calculated in this way, but a more convenient method is to obtain $SS_w$ by subtraction:

$$SS_w = SS_t - SS_b.$$

*Step 4*  Calculate the two variance estimates, or 'mean squares', as they are often called. As usual, the variance is the relevant sum of squares divided by the number of degrees of freedom involved. The number of degrees of freedom for the between-groups variance is, as expected, one less than the number of groups. If there are $k$ groups, the relevant figure is thus $(k-1)$. For each group, the number of degrees of freedom for the calculation of the within-groups variance is one less than the number of observations in the group. Since there are $k$ groups, and $N$ observations in total, the total number of degrees of freedom for the within-groups variance is $(N-k)$. We therefore have

$$s_b^2 = \frac{SS_b}{k-1}$$

$$s_w^2 = \frac{SS_w}{N-k}.$$

*Step 5*  Calculate the ratio of the variance estimates:

$$F = \frac{s_b^2}{s_w^2}.$$

*Step 6* Look in table A8 for the critical value of $F$ for the chosen significance level. Look across the top of the table to find the column corresponding to the number of degrees of freedom associated with the between-groups variance estimate, and then trace the column down to the row corresponding to the number of degrees of freedom associated with the within-groups estimate. Since the alternative hypothesis is that $s_b^2 > s_w^2$, this is a directional or one-tailed test. If the critical value is equalled or exceeded, reject the null hypothesis that all the groups have equal means.

The ANOVA method makes certain assumptions which will be familiar from our discussion of the $t$-test in section 7.2.1.2, namely that the populations from which the samples are derived are normal, and that they are of approximately equal variance. The validity of the normality assumption can be tested by the approximate methods discussed in section 4.3, or by the chi-square test for goodness of fit described in section 9.3, provided that the samples are large enough. Homogeneity of variance can be tested by the method given in section 10.2 above. Fortunately, however, the ANOVA technique is fairly tolerant of all but gross departures from normality and homogeneity of variance.

Let us now work through an example of the application of the ANOVA method. In table 10.1 are given the lengths, in words, of the lines in each of four poems by Dylan Thomas: 'O make me a mask', 'Once it was the colour of saying', 'Not from this anger' and 'The spire cranes' (*Collected Poems 1934–1952*, published by J. M. Dent and Sons, 1952). We shall use the ANOVA method to test for significant differences between the mean line lengths for the four poems at the 5 per cent level. We shall need the following in our further calculations:

$$\Sigma x_1 = 117 \qquad \Sigma x_1^2 = 1\,177 \qquad N_1 = 12$$

$$\Sigma x_2 = 118 \qquad \Sigma x_2^2 = 1\,092 \qquad N_2 = 13$$

$$\Sigma x_3 = 100 \qquad \Sigma x_3^2 = 752 \qquad N_3 = 14$$

$$\Sigma x_4 = 109 \qquad \Sigma x_4^2 = 1\,091 \qquad N_4 = 11$$

$$\Sigma x = 444 \qquad \Sigma x^2 = 4\,112 \qquad N = 50$$

*Step 1*

$$SS_t = \Sigma x^2 - \frac{(\Sigma x)^2}{N} = 4\,112 - \frac{444^2}{50} = 169.28$$

Table 10.1 Line lengths in four poems by Dylan Thomas

| Line lengths (no. of words) in: | | | |
|---|---|---|---|
| Poem 1 'O make me...' (N = 12) | Poem 2 'Once it was...' (N = 13) | Poem 3 'Not from this...' (N = 14) | Poem 4 'The spire...' (N = 11) |
| 13 | 7 | 6 | 8 |
| 9 | 9 | 8 | 10 |
| 9 | 9 | 9 | 10 |
| 10 | 10 | 6 | 11 |
| 7 | 8 | 7 | 10 |
| 10 | 10 | 8 | 9 |
| 11 | 10 | 4 | 9 |
| 9 | 9 | 9 | 11 |
| 9 | 8 | 8 | 11 |
| 9 | 11 | 9 | 11 |
| 8 | 11 | 5 | 9 |
| 13 | 7 | 7 | |
| | 9 | 9 | |
| | | 5 | |

*Step 2*

$$SS_b = \frac{(\Sigma x_1)^2}{N_1} + \frac{(\Sigma x_2)^2}{N_2} + \frac{(\Sigma x_3)^2}{N_3} + \frac{(\Sigma x_4)^2}{N_4} - \frac{(\Sigma x)^2}{N}$$

$$= \frac{117^2}{12} + \frac{118^2}{13} + \frac{100^2}{14} + \frac{109^2}{11} - \frac{444^2}{50} = 63.48.$$

*Step 3*

$$SS_w = SS_t - SS_b = 169.28 - 63.48 = 105.80.$$

*Step 4*

$$s_b^2 = \frac{SS_b}{k-1} = \frac{63.48}{4-1} = 21.16.$$

$$s_w^2 = \frac{SS_w}{N-k} = \frac{105.80}{50-4} = 2.30.$$

**Table 10.2    Summary of analysis of variance for line length in four poems by Dylan Thomas**

| Source of variation | Sums of squares | Degrees of freedom | Variance estimate |
|---|---|---|---|
| Between groups | 63.48 | 3 | 21.16 $(s_b^2)$ |
| Within groups | 105.80 | 46 | 2.30 $(s_w^2)$ |
| Total | 169.28 | 49 | $F = 9.20 \dfrac{s_b^2}{s_w^2}$ |

*Step 5*

$$F = \frac{s_b^2}{s_w^2} = \frac{21.16}{2.30} = 9.20.$$

*Step 6*    We look up the critical value of $F$ for the 5 per cent level, with $(k-1) = 3$ degrees of freedom for the between-groups variance estimate, and $(N-k) = 46$ degrees of freedom for the within-groups estimate. The table does not give us an exact value for 46 degrees of freedom, but we shall not be seriously in error if we take the value for 45 degrees of freedom, giving a critical value of about 2.82 for the situation we are interested in. Our calculated value of 9.20 is much larger than this, so we can conclude that there is a significant difference in the means.

The main quantities in an analysis of variance are often summarised in the form of a table, such as table 10.2.

Three further pieces of work in connection with this small research problem are left as exercises for the reader. We have assumed that the line lengths are normally distributed, with approximately equal variance in the four groups. Although the number of lines in the poems is too small to check each individually for normality, it might be worth checking that the values of line length for all four poems taken together are roughly normally distributed. Secondly, homogeneity of variance can be checked by means of the $F$-test, as outlined in section 10.2. In practice, of course, these checks should be made before the ANOVA test is carried out. Thirdly, comparisons of all six possible pairs of means can be undertaken using the $t$-test for small samples, to see just where the significant differences in means lie. (Readers who are assiduous enough to act on these suggestions should find that the pooled set of 50 lines does indeed have approximately normally distributed lengths, that there is no good evidence for abandoning the homogeneity of variance assumption, and that the mean for poem 3 ('Not from this anger') differs significantly from the others, but that poems 1, 2 and 4 do not differ significantly among themselves.)

In this brief introduction to the analysis of variance technique, we have dealt only with the situation where just one factor differentiates the groups. In our worked example this factor was which poem was involved; it could, however, have been the various levels of complexity of sentences in a recall test, various registers of a language, and so on. The ANOVA technique is not, in fact, restricted to such one-factor investigations, but can be generalised to cover cases where there is more than one factor involved. For instance, in an experiment on sentence recall, we might wish to investigate the effect of both sentence complexity and time elapsed between hearing and repeating the sentences. In such a case, we should want to be able to separate the effects of random sampling variation and the effect of each variable we are interested in. We should also want to know if there was any interaction between the two variables, i.e. sentence complexity and time elapsed. More complex variants of the ANOVA technique allow investigations of this kind, involving two or even more factors, to be analysed statistically. Such complications are, however, beyond the scope of this book. For further details, readers should refer to a standard statistics textbook such as Ferguson (1981).

## Exercises

1   In question 2 of the exercises to chapter 2 were given the lengths of 100 stressed and 100 unstressed syllables in a sample of spoken French. Test whether the variances of stressed and unstressed syllable lengths differ significantly at the 10 per cent level.

2   In question 1 of the exercises to chapter 7 were given the number of word types in each of 50 samples of 500 running words each, from two texts. Test, at the 10 per cent level, whether the variances of the number of types per 500 words differ significantly between the two texts.

3   In a more detailed study of syllable length in French than that referred to in question 1, the lengths were determined (in units of 1/50 sec) for syllables in four different environments:

A ($N = 8$):   unstressed, at beginning of tone group, after no pause

B ($N = 29$):  unstressed, at beginning of tone group, after a pause

C ($N = 50$):  stressed, inside a tone group, inside a mono-syllabic word

D ($N = 17$):  stressed, inside a tone group, at beginning of a polysyllabic word.

A:  16, 18, 17, 18, 12, 17, 17, 8

B:  21, 14, 12, 10, 20, 11, 11, 16, 12, 12, 13, 12, 14, 15, 18, 11, 10, 10, 16, 16, 17, 17, 14, 12, 13, 10, 15, 11, 11

C:  21, 19, 23, 14, 14, 13, 16, 17, 18, 19, 24, 16, 12, 23, 24, 16, 18, 12, 23, 19, 22, 20, 22, 23, 27, 25, 24, 21, 20, 15, 22, 22, 20, 26, 19, 13, 17, 22, 14, 23, 14, 17, 25, 17, 22, 20, 21, 22, 20, 12

D:  15, 15, 16, 21, 18, 10, 18, 16, 15, 13, 18, 16, 16, 19, 16, 16, 16

Use the analysis of variance method to determine whether there are significant differences, at the 5 per cent level, in the mean lengths under the four conditions.

4   A class of 10 German, 9 Japanese, 11 French and 8 Russian students of English is given an exercise on the use of the definite and indefinite articles in English. The number of errors made by the students in each nationality group is as follows:

| German | Japanese | French | Russian |
|--------|----------|--------|---------|
| 4      | 6        | 3      | 5       |
| 6      | 3        | 4      | 3       |
| 8      | 7        | 8      | 10      |
| 2      | 12       | 8      | 7       |
| 3      | 9        | 2      | 6       |
| 1      | 8        | 5      | 8       |
| 4      | 5        | 3      | 9       |
| 5      | 7        | 2      | 10      |
| 3      | 3        | 2      |         |
| 2      |          | 4      |         |
|        |          | 1      |         |

Use the analysis of variance method to determine whether there are significant differences in the means at the 5 per cent level. If there are, go on to perform pairwise $t$-tests to show where the differences lie.

# 11 Correlation

## 11.1 The nature of correlation

Twice in this book, we have had occasion to mention the concept of correlation. In section 6.2.1, we noted a distinction between experimental studies, in which the investigator deliberately manipulates the independent variable in order to test the effect on the dependent variable, and observational or correlational studies, in which he simply observes the relationship, if any, between two (or more) variables. In section 6.3.6, we discussed two types of relation between samples, depending on the design of the investigation: in an independent groups design, two (or more) quite different sets of subjects are used; but in a repeated measures or a matched pairs design, the same set of subjects, or subjects closely matched on some particular variable(s), is involved in the two (or more) conditions of the test. In the latter case, we must allow for the possibility that the results of the test for each subject or matched pair of subjects may reflect some characteristic of that subject or matched pair: in other words, there may be some correlation between the scores, which is due to the properties of the subjects rather than to the independent variable being investigated.

Correlation is, then, that area of statistics which is concerned with the study of systematic relationships between two (or more) variables, and attempts to answer questions such as: Do high values of variable $X$ tend to go together with high values of variable $Y$? Or do high values of $X$ go with low values of $Y$? Or is there some more complex relationship between $X$ and $Y$, or perhaps no relationship at all? In this chapter we shall look briefly at some of the techniques used to answer such questions. We shall deal only with relationships between two variables: details of multiple correlation methods can be found in more advanced statistics textbooks.

## 11.2    Visual representation of correlation: scattergrams

The first step in any study of the possible correlation between two ratio or intervally scaled variables is to produce what is called a *scatter diagram*, or *scattergram*. This is a graph, in which the axes represent values of the two variables, and each member of the sample or population being investigated is represented by a dot or cross whose position is defined by the values of the two variables for that member. Some possible types of scattergram are shown in figures 11.1–11.6. In figure 11.1 we have a strong positive linear correlation between the variables $X$ and $Y$, in that the higher the value of $X$ for a given member of the sample, the higher the value of $Y$ tends to be. The points cluster closely,

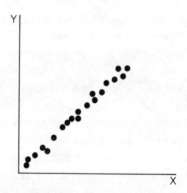

**Figure 11.1    High positive correlation**

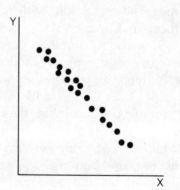

**Figure 11.2    High negative correlation**

**Figure 11.3** Lower positive correlation

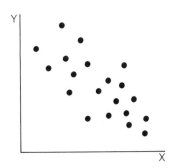

**Figure 11.4** Lower negative correlation

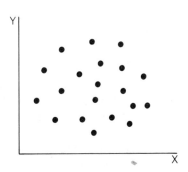

**Figure 11.5** Little or no correlation

and it would be easy to draw a straight line through the middle of them. Figure 11.2 shows strong negative correlation, high values of $X$ being associated with low values of $Y$, and vice versa. Figure 11.3, like figure 11.1, shows positive correlation, but here the correlation is weaker: high values of $X$ still tend to go with

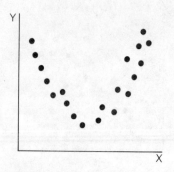

**Figure 11.6    Nonlinear relationship**

high values of $Y$, but there are quite a few exceptions, so that the points do not cluster so strongly round a straight line. Similarly, figure 11.4 shows weaker negative correlation than figure 11.2. In figure 11.5 there is no discernible pattern of dots at all, and the variables thus show little or no correlation. In figure 11.6 there is a very clear pattern of relationship, but it is not linear; rather, there is a more complex curved pattern.

There are two reasons why a scattergram should always be drawn as the first step in any study of correlation. Firstly, and most obviously, the diagram provides a visual indication of whether there is any appreciable correlation, and if so whether it is positive or negative. Secondly, it is important to establish whether or not the pattern of relationship is linear, since, as we shall see, the usual quantitative measures of correlation assume a linear relationship.

We shall now construct a scattergram for the data in table 11.1, which represent the scores of 20 foreign language learners on (a) a language comprehension test and (b) a translation test, for the foreign language into English. We wish to obtain some visual indication of whether there is any systematic relationship between the sets of scores on the two tests.

The scattergram in figure 11.7 shows that there is some degree of positive correlation between the scores on the two tests. The correlation is not extremely strong, since the dots do not cluster very closely round the best straight line which could be constructed to run through the middle of them. In the next section, we shall see how a measure of the degree of correlation can be obtained.

Table 11.1 Marks on comprehension and translation
tests for 20 foreign language learners

| | Score on | |
|---|---|---|
| *Learner no.* | *Comprehension test* | *Translation test* |
| 1 | 17 | 15 |
| 2 | 13 | 13 |
| 3 | 12 | 8 |
| 4 | 14 | 17 |
| 5 | 15 | 16 |
| 6 | 8 | 9 |
| 7 | 9 | 14 |
| 8 | 13 | 10 |
| 9 | 11 | 16 |
| 10 | 14 | 13 |
| 11 | 12 | 14 |
| 12 | 16 | 17 |
| 13 | 10 | 9 |
| 14 | 18 | 16 |
| 15 | 15 | 19 |
| 16 | 16 | 16 |
| 17 | 12 | 17 |
| 18 | 16 | 12 |
| 19 | 10 | 14 |
| 20 | 9 | 8 |

## 11.3 The quantitative assessment of correlation: correlation coefficients

### 11.3.1 Some general remarks on correlation coefficients

Although a scattergram is an important first step in a study of correlation between two variables with an interval or ratio level of measurement, it does not give any precise quantitative assessment of the degree of correlation involved. To supplement the information given by a scattergram, a descriptive statistic known as a *correlation coefficient* is normally calculated. The expressions for calculating such coefficients are so devised that a value of +1 is obtained for perfect positive correlation, a value of −1 for perfect negative correlation, and a value of zero for no correlation at all. For interval or ratio variables, the appropriate measure is

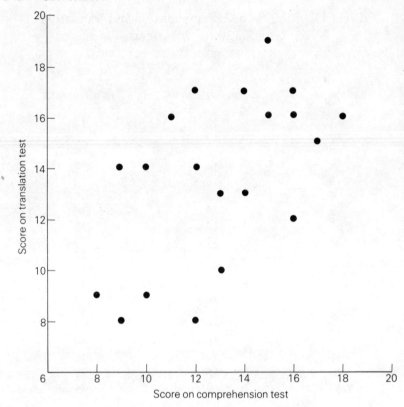

**Figure 11.7    Scattergram of scores on two language tests**

the so-called *Pearson product–moment correlation coefficient*, which takes into account the exact magnitude of each score on each variable.

For ordinal variables, scattergrams are not really appropriate, since any attempt to demonstrate a linear relationship assumes measurement on a scale with equal intervals. A measure of the correlation between two ordinal variables can, however, be obtained by calculating the *Spearman rank correlation coefficient*, which is based solely on the ranking of the observations. For certain types of investigation involving nominal variables, a third kind of correlation coefficient, the *phi coefficient*, may be used.

Each of the three types of correlation coefficient will now be discussed in turn.

## 11.3.2 The Pearson product–moment correlation coefficient

As stated above, the Pearson correlation coefficient is appropriate where both variables under consideration are of the ratio or interval type. Its use also assumes that each set of scores is normally distributed.

If we represent the score of any member of the sample on one of the variables as $x$, and the corresponding score on the other variable as $y$, then the set of $x$-scores will have a mean and a standard deviation given by

$$\bar{x} = \frac{\Sigma x}{N} \qquad s_x = \sqrt{\frac{\Sigma(x-\bar{x})^2}{N-1}}$$

where $N$ is the number of pairs of observations. Similarly, the $y$-scores will have a mean and standard deviation given by

$$\bar{y} = \frac{\Sigma y}{N} \qquad s_y = \sqrt{\frac{\Sigma(y-\bar{y})^2}{N-1}}.$$

Any particular $x$-score can now be expressed in terms of its distance in standard deviations from the mean (that is, as a $z$-score):

$$z_x = \frac{x-\bar{x}}{s_x}.$$

Similarly for any $y$-score:

$$z_y = \frac{y-\bar{y}}{s_y}.$$

The Pearson correlation coefficient is defined as

$$r = \frac{\Sigma z_x z_y}{N-1}$$

where $\Sigma z_x z_y$ is the sum of the products of the two $z$-scores, and acts as a measure of the relationship between the two variables $x$ and $y$, and $(N-1)$ is the number of degrees of freedom associated with the coefficient. It can be shown that the value of this expression lies between +1 (for perfect positive correlation) and −1 (for perfect negative correlation), as required.

The value of the correlation coefficient $r$ could, of course, be calculated by finding the $z$-scores on each variable for each member of the sample, multiplying them, summing the products over the whole sample, and dividing by $(N-1)$. However, by combining the above equations and rearranging the result, it can be shown that $r$ is also given by the following expression, which is more convenient computationally:

$$r = \frac{N\Sigma xy - \Sigma x \Sigma y}{\sqrt{\{N\Sigma x^2 - (\Sigma x)^2\}\{N\Sigma y^2 - (\Sigma y)^2\}}}.$$

Let us now calculate $r$ for the two sets of language test scores for which we drew a scattergram in figure 11.7. Table 11.2 gives each pair of scores, together with their squares and product, since these are the quantities we need for the calculation of $r$. Substituting in the equation for $r$, we have

$$r = \frac{(20 \times 3\,651) - (260 \times 273)}{\sqrt{\{(20 \times 3\,540) - 260^2\}\{(20 \times 3\,937) - 273^2\}}}$$

$$= \frac{73\,020 - 70\,980}{\sqrt{(70\,800 - 67\,600)(78\,740 - 74\,529)}}$$

$$= \frac{2\,040}{\sqrt{3\,200 \times 4\,211}} = \frac{2\,040}{3\,670.86} = 0.56.$$

As we saw from the scattergram, the two variables are positively correlated, though not extremely strongly.

The question which now arises is just how great the correlation coefficient must be in order that we may claim a significant correlation between the variables. We may set up a null hypothesis that there is no correlation between the two variables: that is, that for the population from which the sample was drawn, the value of $r$ is zero. The question is now, how large must the coefficient be for there to be, say, a 5 per cent chance or less of obtaining the observed result with a sample of $N$ pairs drawn from a population in which there is actually no correlation? Table A9 of appendix 1 gives the critical values of $r$ for various numbers of pairs of observations, $N$. For our language test scores we have $N = 20$, and the

Table 11.2    The language test scores and their squares and products

|  | Scores on |  |  |  |
|---|---|---|---|---|

| Comprehension (x) | Translátion (y) | $x^2$ | $y^2$ | $xy$ |
|---|---|---|---|---|
| 17 | 15 | 289 | 225 | 255 |
| 13 | 13 | 169 | 169 | 169 |
| 12 | 8 | 144 | 64 | 96 |
| 14 | 17 | 196 | 289 | 238 |
| 15 | 16 | 225 | 256 | 240 |
| 8 | 9 | 64 | 81 | 72 |
| 9 | 14 | 81 | 196 | 126 |
| 13 | 10 | 169 | 100 | 130 |
| 11 | 16 | 121 | 256 | 176 |
| 14 | 13 | 196 | 169 | 182 |
| 12 | 14 | 144 | 196 | 168 |
| 16 | 17 | 256 | 289 | 272 |
| 10 | 9 | 100 | 81 | 90 |
| 18 | 16 | 324 | 256 | 288 |
| 15 | 19 | 225 | 361 | 285 |
| 16 | 16 | 256 | 256 | 256 |
| 12 | 17 | 144 | 289 | 204 |
| 16 | 12 | 256 | 144 | 192 |
| 10 | 14 | 100 | 196 | 140 |
| 9 | 8 | 81 | 64 | 72 |
| $\Sigma x = 260$ | $\Sigma y = 273$ | $\Sigma x^2 = 3540$ | $\Sigma y^2 = 3937$ | $\Sigma xy = 3651$ |

critical value of $r$ at the 5 per cent level in a non-directional test (that is, if our alternative hypothesis is simply that the two variables are correlated) is 0.444, while that in a directional test (that is, if our alternative hypothesis is that there is positive correlation) is 0.378. Therefore, whichever alternative hypothesis we have set up, the correlation coefficient is in fact significant at the 5 per cent level.

### 11.3.3    The Spearman rank correlation coefficient

If both of the variables whose correlation we wish to test are ordinal, the appropriate measure is, as we have seen, the Spearman coefficient, based on ranking. If one variable is ordinal and the other interval or ratio, then the interval or ratio data may be treated as ordinal by using only their rank ordering (with a consequent loss of information), so that the Spearman method can be used.

We first rank the set of $N$ scores on the first variable from smallest (1) to largest ($N$). Similarly, we rank the set of scores on the other variable, again from 1 to $N$. Where there are ties (that is, where there is the same value on a given variable for two or more members of the sample), we use the mean of the ranks that would have been occupied if no tie had occurred. (Compare the similar procedure in the Mann–Whitney and Wilcoxon tests; see chapter 8.) For each pair of scores, we then calculate the difference ($d$) between the ranks, and square it. The Spearman correlation coefficient $\rho$ (the Greek letter 'rho') is then calculated as

$$\rho = 1 - \frac{6\Sigma d^2}{N(N^2 - 1)}.$$

Table A10 of appendix 1 gives critical values of $\rho$ for various numbers of pairs of observations, $N$.

Let us now work through an example of the use of the Spearman correlation coefficient. Suppose that we have asked a panel of five ten-year-old children to rate ten passages of English according to how difficult they found them to read, on a scale from 1 (extremely easy) to 10 (extremely difficult). Suppose also that we have asked a panel of five teachers to rate the same passages according to how difficult they think the passages would be for ten-year-old children to read, again on a scale from 1 to 10. We then take, to the nearest whole number, the median rating for each passage, by each group, with the results shown in table 11.3. The question is whether the two sets of ratings are significantly correlated at, let us say, the 5 per cent level. We shall predict that they are indeed positively correlated, and therefore need a directional test of significance for the correlation coefficient.

To calculate $\rho$ we first rank each set of ratings, remembering to allocate the mean rank to any groups of tied scores. We then calculate the difference between ranks for each passage of English, and square it. Summation over all ten passages gives $\Sigma d^2$. These operations are shown in table 11.4.

We can now calculate $\rho$ as follows:

$$\rho = 1 - \frac{6 \times 20.5}{10(10^2 - 1)} = 0.88.$$

Table 11.3 Median ratings of reading difficulty for ten passages, by panels of children and teachers

|  | Median rating | |
|---|---|---|
| *Passage number* | *by children* | *by teachers* |
| 1 | 7 | 5 |
| 2 | 6 | 4 |
| 3 | 4 | 5 |
| 4 | 5 | 6 |
| 5 | 8 | 10 |
| 6 | 7 | 7 |
| 7 | 10 | 9 |
| 8 | 3 | 2 |
| 9 | 9 | 8 |
| 10 | 2 | 1 |

Table 11.4 Ranking of the sets of difficulty ratings and calculation of $\Sigma d^2$

| *Median rating by children* | *Rank* | *Median rating by teachers* | *Rank* | *Rank difference (d)* | $d^2$ |
|---|---|---|---|---|---|
| 7 | 6.5 | 5 | 4.5 | 2 | 4 |
| 6 | 5 | 4 | 3 | 2 | 4 |
| 4 | 3 | 5 | 4.5 | −1.5 | 2.25 |
| 5 | 4 | 6 | 6 | −2 | 4 |
| 8 | 8 | 10 | 10 | −2 | 4 |
| 7 | 6.5 | 7 | 7 | −0.5 | 0.25 |
| 10 | 10 | 9 | 9 | 1 | 1 |
| 3 | 2 | 2 | 2 | 0 | 0 |
| 9 | 9 | 8 | 8 | 1 | 1 |
| 2 | 1 | 1 | 1 | 0 | 0 |
| | | | | | $\Sigma d^2 = 20.5$ |

Table A10 shows that the critical value of $\rho$ for $N = 10$ in a directional test is 0.564. There is therefore a significant correlation between the children's and teachers' ratings at this level (indeed, the value of $\rho$ is significant even at the 1 per cent level).

The Spearman correlation coefficient becomes an inaccurate measure if there is a large number of tied ranks. Under these circumstances, a more accurate method is to use the ranks as values (with mean ranks for the tied observations) to calculate a Pearson coefficient (see section 11.3.2).

### 11.3.4    The phi coefficient

Where the two variables we are concerned with are nominal, the question of whether they are correlated or not resolves itself into the question, 'If a particular item has property A, is there a high probability that it will also have property B?' A common application is to the statistics of testing in language teaching and other fields. Here the question at issue is, 'If a learner passes on test item 1, is he also likely to pass on item 2?' The general situation involved in such studies can be represented as a 2 X 2 table.

| *Variable 2* | *Variable 1* | |
|---|---|---|
| | − | + |
| + | *A* | *B* |
| − | *C* | *D* |

Here, $A$, $B$, $C$ and $D$ are the frequencies of observations in the four cells of the table; for instance, $A$ might be the number of learners who fail test item 1 but pass test item 2, $B$ the number who pass both test items, and so on. The correlation between the two variables can be measured by the phi ($\phi$) coefficient, defined as

$$\phi = \frac{BC - AD}{\sqrt{(A+B)(C+D)(A+C)(B+D)}}.$$

It should be clear from this formula that the phi coefficient is very closely related to the chi-square statistic discussed in chapter 9. The two statistics are in fact related as follows:

$$\phi = \sqrt{\chi^2/N} \qquad \text{or} \qquad \chi^2 = N\phi^2.$$

The significance of a phi coefficient can therefore be assessed by calculating $N\phi^2$ and then looking up critical values in the chi-

Table 11.5 Success and failure on two language test items

| Test item 2 | Test item 1 | | |
|---|---|---|---|
| | Failure | Success | Total |
| Success | 49 | 21 | 70 |
| Failure | 14 | 16 | 30 |
| Total | 63 | 37 | 100 |

square table (table A7) with one degree of freedom (since we have a 2 × 2 table: see section 9.4).

Let us suppose that we wish to know whether success on one item in a language test is significantly correlated with success on a second item. Imagine that we have tested 100 learners, with the results shown in table 11.5. We calculate $\phi$ as

$$\phi = \frac{(21 \times 14) - (49 \times 16)}{\sqrt{70 \times 30 \times 63 \times 37}} = -0.22.$$

There is thus some degree of negative correlation between the two variables. To test its significance at the 5 per cent level, we calculate

$$\chi^2 = N\phi^2 = 100 \times (-0.22)^2 = 4.84.$$

The critical value of $\chi^2$ for one degree of freedom and the 5 per cent level is 3.84, so that the calculated value of $\phi$ is in fact significant at this level.

## 11.4 The interpretation of correlation: a caveat

It is extremely important to realise that even a very significantly high correlation coefficient between scores on two variables does not mean that the phenomena concerned are related in a cause-and-effect manner. For instance, if we were to select 50 learners of French from a whole school, simply on the basis of their height, making sure that we obtained a full range of heights from shortest to tallest, it is quite likely that we should find some degree of positive correlation between height and performance on a battery of French tests. It would not be sensible, however, to conclude that height in itself is a factor in determining proficiency in French: clearly, there is a third variable – age – which is correlated with both height and language proficiency. It must never be forgotten, then, that the statistical study of correlation merely tests for a significant *mathematical* relationship between values for the variables concerned. It will not tell us how such correlations should be interpreted; still less will it give us direct information about causes and their effects.

**Exercises**

1   Twenty pupils in the same year of a school are learning both French and German. Their results in the end of year examinations are as given in table 11.6.

   (i)   Draw a scattergram of the data.
   (ii)  The investigator predicts a positive correlation between the two sets of scores. Is there good evidence for this?

**Table 11.6**

|  | Marks out of 100 | |
| --- | --- | --- |
| Pupil no. | French | German |
| 1 | 72 | 63 |
| 2 | 48 | 40 |
| 3 | 34 | 61 |
| 4 | 58 | 52 |
| 5 | 80 | 68 |
| 6 | 41 | 54 |
| 7 | 35 | 30 |
| 8 | 55 | 54 |
| 9 | 61 | 52 |
| 10 | 60 | 49 |
| 11 | 74 | 80 |
| 12 | 45 | 49 |
| 13 | 48 | 51 |
| 14 | 50 | 47 |
| 15 | 58 | 45 |
| 16 | 63 | 61 |
| 17 | 56 | 50 |
| 18 | 64 | 60 |
| 19 | 28 | 41 |
| 20 | 59 | 58 |

2  A panel of teachers is asked to grade the reading and writing
   abilities of 15 children on a scale from 1 (very poor) to 7
   (excellent), with the results given in table 11.7. Calculate the
   value of an appropriate correlation coefficient, and determine
   whether it is significant at the 5 per cent level.

**Table 11.7**

| Child no. | Ability in | |
|---|---|---|
| | Reading | Writing |
| 1 | 3 | 6 |
| 2 | 4 | 4 |
| 3 | 5 | 3 |
| 4 | 6 | 7 |
| 5 | 3 | 4 |
| 6 | 4 | 2 |
| 7 | 3 | 5 |
| 8 | 5 | 6 |
| 9 | 2 | 3 |
| 10 | 4 | 5 |
| 11 | 7 | 3 |
| 12 | 5 | 4 |
| 13 | 6 | 4 |
| 14 | 2 | 3 |
| 15 | 3 | 2 |

3  In a study of the relationship between politeness and speech
   act classification in directives (Butler, 1982), a large number of
   informants were asked to classify directives as orders, requests
   or suggestions, and also to rate each directive on a scale of
   politeness in a given social context, from 1 (very impolite) to
   7 (very polite). The median politeness ratings and the percentage of informants classifying each directive as an order,
   a request and a suggestion are given in table 11.8. It was predicted that there would be a positive correlation between
   politeness and classification as a request, a negative correlation
   between politeness and classification as an order, and zero
   correlation between politeness and classification as a suggestion.
   For each speech act class, draw a scattergram showing its
   relation to median politeness rating, calculate the value of the
   Pearson correlation coefficient, and determine its significance
   at the 5 per cent level. (*Note:* Where the percentages given for
   a particular directive do not add up to 100, this is because a

**Table 11.8**

| Directive number | Median politeness rating | % of informants classifying directive as | | |
|---|---|---|---|---|
| | | Order | Request | Suggestion |
| 1 | 1.04 | 96 | 0 | 0 |
| 2 | 1.09 | 86 | 0 | 1 |
| 3 | 1.32 | 97 | 1 | 1 |
| 4 | 1.82 | 36 | 4 | 54 |
| 5 | 2.15 | 27 | 11 | 61 |
| 6 | 2.19 | 38 | 13 | 47 |
| 7 | 2.29 | 37 | 4 | 55 |
| 8 | 2.85 | 12 | 4 | 75 |
| 9 | 1.36 | 95 | 4 | 1 |
| 10 | 2.64 | 40 | 36 | 10 |
| 11 | 2.83 | 34 | 42 | 8 |
| 12 | 3.67 | 19 | 69 | 2 |
| 13 | 3.99 | 15 | 74 | 7 |
| 14 | 4.20 | 13 | 82 | 2 |
| 15 | 4.70 | 13 | 81 | 4 |
| 16 | 2.12 | 16 | 39 | 31 |
| 17 | 3.02 | 4 | 3 | 89 |
| 18 | 3.37 | 4 | 15 | 75 |
| 19 | 3.65 | 4 | 70 | 23 |
| 20 | 3.77 | 2 | 54 | 36 |
| 21 | 4.73 | 3 | 95 | 2 |
| 22 | 4.94 | 7 | 79 | 13 |
| 23 | 5.62 | 4 | 94 | 2 |
| 24 | 5.64 | 4 | 85 | 10 |
| 25 | 1.64 | 50 | 31 | 1 |
| 26 | 2.66 | 32 | 36 | 13 |
| 27 | 2.74 | 34 | 39 | 9 |
| 28 | 3.18 | 69 | 23 | 4 |
| 29 | 5.96 | 1 | 81 | 13 |
| 30 | 6.62 | 0 | 76 | 18 |
| 31 | 6.46 | 1 | 79 | 18 |
| 32 | 6.74 | 1 | 84 | 12 |
| 33 | 1.12 | 89 | 0 | 0 |
| 34 | 1.62 | 86 | 3 | 3 |
| 35 | 1.08 | 46 | 17 | 22 |

few informants either did not accept the directive at all, or omitted to rate it.)

4   In a study of child language by Wells (1977), 20 children were ranked on each of three measures: an index of language use, a reading test, and social class of the family. The rankings are

Table 11.9

| Child | Language use | Reading | Social class |
|---|---|---|---|
| Alan | 11 | 16 | 18 |
| Andrew | 4 | 15 | 13 |
| Ann | 10 | 7 | 15.5 |
| David | 1 | 13 | 2.5 |
| Derek | 8 | 9 | 8.5 |
| Elizabeth | 2 | 6 | 6 |
| George | 20 | 20 | 20 |
| James | 9 | 2 | 10.5 |
| Jane | 14 | 17 | 15.5 |
| Janet | 15 | 11 | 13 |
| John | 3 | 3 | 2.5 |
| Judy | 19 | 8 | 10.5 |
| Kathleen | 13 | 14 | 8.5 |
| Mary | 18 | 12 | 18 |
| Paul | 12 | 19 | 18 |
| Peter | 5 | 10 | 13 |
| Philip | 17 | 18 | 5 |
| Sandra | 6 | 5 | 2.5 |
| Susan | 7 | 1 | 7 |
| Wendy | 16 | 4 | 2.5 |

given in table 11.9. Calculate values of the Spearman correlation coefficient for

(i)   language use against reading;
(ii)  language use against social class;
(iii) reading against social class;

and assess their significance at the 5 per cent level.

5   In a study of the pronunciation of words like *car*, 60 men and 40 women from an American city are tested to determine whether or not they predominantly use a postvocalic /r/. The results are as follows:

| | | Predominantly use postvocalic /r/ | |
|---|---|---|---|
| | | − | + |
| Male | + | 36 | 24 |
| | − | 11 | 29 |

Calculate the phi-coefficient for these data, determine its significance at the 5 per cent level, and interpret the result.

# 12 Statistics, computers and calculators

## 12.1 Introduction

It must be admitted that many of the statistical procedures discussed in this book involve quite lengthy and tedious calculations, in the course of which human calculators are likely to make the occasional error. It is not surprising, then, that much statistical work is now carried out by means of computers. Space does not permit more than a brief discussion of this aspect of the use of computers in language study: readers are referred to the companion volume to this book (Butler, 1985) for a survey of computing in linguistic and literary studies.

Fortunately, researchers who wish to use a computer to relieve them of some of the drudgery of statistical calculations can often do so without having to learn to program the machine in one of the so-called 'high-level' computer languages such as BASIC, FORTRAN or PASCAL. Because statistical calculations are a common requirement of a wide range of users, 'package' programs have been developed, which allow users to specify their needs in terms that are not too far removed from ordinary English; the translation of these instructions into a form on which the computer can act directly is something that they need know nothing about. In this concluding chapter, the use of two widely available statistical packages, the Statistical Package for the Social Sciences (SPSS) and Minitab, will be illustrated, using some of the examples worked through manually in previous chapters. There then follows a brief review of the usefulness of the simple electronic calculator in statistical work.

## 12.2    The Statistical Package for the Social Sciences (SPSS)

SPSS is an extremely comprehensive statistical analysis package, supported on a wide range of computers. As the name suggests, it was designed primarily for use by social scientists, and the concept on which SPSS analyses are based, namely the 'case', reflects this orientation. A 'case' in a sociological study might represent a particular member of the human group under investigation, together with values for various attributes such as age, sex, social class and the like. Clearly, such a concept is directly applicable also to some kinds of sociolinguistic study. In other types of linguistic and literary investigation the 'case' concept is less clearly relevant; however, with a little thought the data can usually be expressed in a form suitable for application of the package.

SPSS will produce frequency distributions, bar charts and descriptive statistics (mean, median, mode, range, standard deviation, standard error). It will allow cross-tabulation of data in contingency tables, and performance of chi-square tests to assess the degree of association of variables. Parametric tests (the *t*-test for independent or correlated samples, analysis of variance) and a range of non-parametric tests (including the Mann–Whitney, Wilcoxon signed-ranks and sign tests) are available. Scattergrams can be produced, and Pearson or Spearman correlation coefficients calculated. More sophisticated analyses which are beyond the scope of this book can also be carried out. An overview of the facilities offered can be found in the introductory guide by Norušis (1982). In addition to the normal 'batch' mode version of SPSS, in which output from the analysis goes either to the lineprinter or to a named file, there is a version which allows the 'conversational' or 'interactive' use of the package, the results of the analysis being sent directly to the terminal at which the user is working.

As our first example of the use of SPSS, let us take the production of a frequency distribution table and descriptive statistics for the scores of class A in the language test situation discussed in chapters 2 and 3 (for data, see table 2.1). A suitable set of SPSS commands is shown in figure 12.1. The RUN NAME command simply gives a title to the analysis. The package is then informed that only one variable, called SCORE, is involved. It is also told that the input data are in free format; that is, they are strung out along one or more lines, individual data items being separated by blanks. There are 30 cases (in this example, a case is just the score for one language learner). The VAR LABELS command specifies that the full title 'SCORE ON LANGUAGE TEST' is to be associated with the variable SCORE. The FREQUENCIES command says that it is the variable SCORE that is to be analysed. In the STATISTICS command, options 1, 3, 4, 5 and 9 are selected: these correspond to the mean, median, mode, standard deviation and range, respectively. The package is then instructed to read the input data, which follow the read command. The end of the data is signalled, and the FINISH command terminates the run. Figure 12.2 shows the frequency distribution table and statistics which are printed in response to these commands. Note that the frequency distribution table gives relative frequencies, cumulative frequencies and frequencies adjusted for any missing values (of which there are none in the present analysis), as well as the absolute frequencies. The values calculated for the descriptive statistics agree with those calculated in chapter 3.

As a second example of the usefulness of SPSS, consider the *t*-test used in section 7.2.1.2 to assess the significance of differences in the correctness of recall of sentences by two independent groups of subjects, tested under different conditions (for data, see table 7.2). The SPSS commands and data are shown in figure 12.3. The package is told that two variables, GROUP and RECALL, are involved: in the later VAR LABELS command these are associated with the full titles 'CONDITION OF TEST' and 'SENTENCES RECALLED CORRECTLY', respectively. Further, the VALUE LABELS command specifies that scores from Group 1 are identified in the data by the code 1, and scores from Group 2 by the

```
RUN NAME         LANGUAGE TEST SCORES, GROUP A
VARIABLE LIST    SCORE
INPUT FORMAT     FREEFIELD
N OF CASES       30
VAR LABELS       SCORE ON LANGUAGE TEST/
FREQUENCIES      GENERAL = SCORE
STATISTICS       1 3 4 5 9
READ INPUT DATA
15 12 11 18 15 15 9 19 14 13 11 12 18 15 16 14 16 17 15 17 13 14 13 15 17
19 17 18 16 14
END INPUT DATA
FINISH
```

**Figure 12.1    SPSS commands and data for analysis of language test scores**

SCORE     ON LANGUAGE TEST

| CATEGORY LABEL | CODE | ABSOLUTE FREQ | RELATIVE FREQ (PCT) | ADJUSTED FREQ (PCT) | CUM FREQ (PCT) |
|---|---|---|---|---|---|
| | 9. | 1 | 3.3 | 3.3 | 3.3 |
| | 11. | 2 | 6.7 | 6.7 | 10.0 |
| | 12. | 2 | 6.7 | 6.7 | 16.7 |
| | 13. | 3 | 10.0 | 10.0 | 26.7 |
| | 14. | 4 | 13.3 | 13.3 | 40.0 |
| | 15. | 6 | 20.0 | 20.0 | 60.0 |
| | 16. | 3 | 10.0 | 10.0 | 70.0 |
| | 17. | 4 | 13.3 | 13.3 | 83.3 |
| | 18. | 3 | 10.0 | 10.0 | 93.3 |
| | 19. | 2 | 6.7 | 6.7 | 100.0 |
| | TOTAL | 30 | 100.0 | 100.0 | |

| MEAN | 14.933 | MEDIAN | 15.000 | MODE | 15.000 |
|---|---|---|---|---|---|
| STD DEV | 2.490 | RANGE | 10.000 | | |

| VALID CASES | 30 | MISSING CASES | 0 |
|---|---|---|---|

LANGUAGE TEST SCORES, GROUP A

**Figure 12.2    SPSS output for analysis of language test scores**

```
VARIABLE LIST     GROUP RECALL
INPUT FORMAT      FREEFIELD
N OF CASES        19
VAR LABELS        GROUP CONDITION OF TEST/
                  RECALL SENTENCES RECALLED CORRECTLY/
VALUE LABELS      GROUP (1) CONDITION 1 (2) CONDITION 2
T-TEST            GROUPS=GROUP/VARIABLES=RECALL
READ INPUT DATA
1 18 1 15 1 13 1 17 1 14 1 8 1 10 1 11 1 7 1 17 2 13 2 14 2 12 2 6 2 11
2 13 2 17 2 16 2 5
END INPUT DATA
FINISH
```

**Figure 12.3    SPSS commands and data for *t*-test on sentence recall**

code 2. The INPUT FORMAT is specified as free, so that the data consist of a set of scores, each with its associated group coding (1 or 2), separated by blanks. The number of scores is given as 19 for the two groups taken together. A *t*-test is requested, with the groups for comparison being selected on the GROUP coding, and RECALL as the variable under test. The output (see figure 12.4) gives a number of pieces of information about the data. The number of cases, and the mean, standard deviation and standard

T-TEST

GROUP 1 – GROUP   EQ   1.
GROUP 2 – GROUP   EQ   2.

| VARIABLE | NUMBER OF CASES | MEAN | STANDARD DEVIATION | STANDARD ERROR |
|---|---|---|---|---|
| RECALL | SENTENCES RECALLED CORRECTLY | | | |
| GROUP 1 | 10 | 13.0000 | 3.887 | 1.229 |
| GROUP 2 | 9 | 11.8889 | 4.076 | 1.359 |

| | POOLED VARIANCE ESTIMATE | | | SEPARATE VARIANCE ESTIMATE | | |
|---|---|---|---|---|---|---|
| F VALUE | 2-TAIL PROB. | T VALUE | DEGREES OF FREEDOM | 2-TAIL PROB. | | |
| 1.10 | 0.883 | 0.61 | 17 | 0.551 | | |

| POOLED VARIANCE ESTIMATE | | | SEPARATE VARIANCE ESTIMATE | | |
|---|---|---|---|---|---|
| T VALUE | DEGREES OF FREEDOM | 2-TAIL PROB. | T VALUE | DEGREES OF FREEDOM | 2-TAIL PROB. |
| 0.61 | 17 | 0.551 | 0.61 | 16.58 | 0.552 |

**Figure 12.4   SPSS analysis output for *t*-test on sentence recall data**

error for the variable under test (here, the number of sentences recalled correctly) are given for each group, and the *F* ratio computed to test for homogeneity of variance. The probability of obtaining the calculated *F* value or a greater value is high (0.883), so that we have no cause to abandon the homogeneity of variance assumption. Two *t*-values are calculated, one based on a pooled variance estimate, as in the method discussed in chapter 7, the other based on separate variance estimates for the two groups, a technique (not discussed in this book) for cases where the variances of the two groups differ considerably. In the present case, as we have seen, the variances are very similar, so it is not surprising that the *t*-values arrived at by the two methods are equal. The slight difference between the value given by SPSS (0.61) and that calculated in chapter 7 (0.60) is due simply to the effect of rounding error. As the *t*-value calculated has a probability of 0.551 of being reached, we have no grounds for rejecting the null hypothesis that the two groups are from distributions with the same mean.

As a third example, consider the use of the Wilcoxon signed-ranks test to assess the significance of differences in the numbers of mistakes made by ten subjects in translating two passages of English into French. This problem was discussed in section 8.3 (for data, see table 8.3). The SPSS commands and data are shown in figure 12.5. A name is given to the run, and the package is told that two variables, named PA and PB, are involved. The format of the data is specified as free, and there are ten cases (that is, ten pairs of scores, each corresponding to one subject). The labels PA and PB are to be associated with the names 'PASSAGE A' and 'PASSAGE B', for use in the labelling of the output. A Wilcoxon

```
RUN NAME        TRANSLATION ERRORS IN TWO PASSAGES OF ENGLISH TO FRENCH
VARIABLE LIST   PA PB
INPUT FORMAT    FREEFIELD
N OF CASES      10
VAR LABELS      PA PASSAGE A
                PB PASSAGE B
NPAR TESTS      WILCOXON = PA WITH PB
READ INPUT DATA
8  10  7  6  4  4  2  5  4  7  10  11  17  15  3  6  2  3  11  14
END INPUT DATA
FINISH
```

Figure 12.5    SPSS commands and data for Wilcoxon test on translation errors

WILCOXON MATCHED-PAIRS SIGNED-RANKS TEST

PA                    PASSAGE A
WITH PB

| CASES | TIES | 2 −RANKS<br>MEAN | 7 +RANKS<br>MEAN | Z | 2-TAILED P |
|---|---|---|---|---|---|
| 10 | 1 | 3.25 | 5.50 | −1.896 | 0.058 |

TRANSLATION ERRORS IN TWO PASSAGES OF ENGLISH TO FRENCH

**Figure 12.6    SPSS analysis output for Wilcoxon test on translation errors**

test of passage A against passage B is requested. The input data are read in, and the run terminated. The results are shown in figure 12.6. The package in fact calculates a $z$-score based on the formula given in section 8.3, even though the number of pairs is considerably smaller than the 20 or so normally considered necessary for testing using the $z$-score method. The probability of obtaining the calculated value or a more extreme one is given as 0.058, so that we cannot reject, at the 5 per cent level, the null hypothesis that the two sets of scores share the same distribution, although the value is very near to the critical region.

As a final example, let us take the problem, discussed in chapter 9, of testing the degree of association between sentence length (long, medium or short) and which of three novels the sentence occurs in (for data, see table 9.5). The SPSS commands and data are shown in figure 12.7. A name is given to the analysis, and the package is then informed that the data are presented in fixed format, rather than in the free format used in earlier examples. The frequency for a particular cell in table 9.5 is in positions 1 to 3 in the data line, a numerical coding for the length of sentence (see below) is in position 5, and a further coding representing the novel concerned is in position 7. The WEIGHT command instructs the package to treat the frequency in each cell as representing that number of individual cases, each of the same kind. The variable LENGTH is to be associated with the longer name 'LENGTH OF SENTENCE'. There are three codings for LENGTH: 1 represents a short sentence, 2 a medium-length sentence, and 3 a long sentence. Similarly, the codes 1, 2 and 3 are used to represent novels 1, 2 and 3, respectively. A cross-tabulation (that is, production of a contingency table) of the sentence length variable by the novel variable is requested. The STATISTICS command selects option 1,

```
RUN NAME        SENTENCE LENGTH IN THREE NOVELS
DATA LIST       FIXED/1    FREQ 1-3   LENGTH 5   NOVEL 7
WEIGHT          FREQ
VAR LABELS      LENGTH, LENGTH OF SENTENCE/
VALUE LABELS    LENGTH (1) SHORT (2) MEDIUM (3) LONG/
                NOVEL (1) NOVEL 1 (2) NOVEL 2 (3) NOVEL 3/
CROSSTABS       TABLES = LENGTH BY NOVEL
STATISTICS      1
READ INPUT DATA
103  1  1
 82  1  2
110  1  3
281  2  1
262  2  2
276  2  3
116  3  1
145  3  2
124  3  3
END INPUT DATA
FINISH
```

Figure 12.7 SPSS commands and data for cross-tabulation and chi-square analysis of sentence length in three novels

which is in fact the chi-square test. The data are read in, and the analysis terminated. The contingency table and chi-square result produced are shown in figure 12.8; the slight difference between the chi-square value and that calculated in chapter 9 is due to rounding error. SPSS gives the probability of obtaining a chi-square value greater than or equal to the calculated value. Since this is 0.085 7, we cannot reject, at the 5 per cent level, the null hypothesis of no association. This is, of course, the conclusion we reached in chapter 9.

## 12.3 The Minitab package

Minitab was designed at the Pennsylvania State University, as an all-purpose, flexible data manipulation package for users with little statistical or computational knowledge. Like SPSS, it is available on a wide range of computers. Minitab is perhaps rather easier to use than SPSS: it is based on a 'worksheet' of rows and columns of data, rather than on the 'case' principle, and the instructions to the package are rather simpler and more transparent than those for SPSS. Minitab has facilities for performing arithmetical operations (such as adding the contents of two columns), for editing, for

```
************************* CROSSTABULATION OF ************************
    LENGTH        LENGTH OF SENTENCE                    BY NOVEL
*********************************************************************
```

| COUNT<br>ROW PCT<br>COL PCT<br>TOT PCT | NOVEL<br>NOVEL 1<br><br>1. | NOVEL 2<br><br>2. | NOVEL 3<br><br>3. | ROW<br>TOTAL |
|---|---|---|---|---|
| **LENGTH** | | | | |
| 1.<br>SHORT | 103<br>34.9<br>20.6<br>6.9 | 82<br>27.8<br>16.8<br>5.5 | 110<br>37.3<br>21.6<br>7.3 | 295<br>19.7 |
| 2.<br>MEDIUM | 281<br>34.3<br>56.2<br>18.7 | 262<br>32.0<br>53.6<br>17.5 | 276<br>33.7<br>54.1<br>18.4 | 819<br>54.6 |
| 3.<br>LONG | 116<br>30.1<br>23.2<br>7.7 | 145<br>37.7<br>29.7<br>9.7 | 124<br>32.2<br>24.3<br>8.3 | 385<br>25.7 |
| COLUMN<br>TOTAL | 500<br>33.4 | 489<br>32.6 | 510<br>34.0 | 1499<br>100.0 |

CHI SQUARE = 8.16640 WITH 4 DEGREES OF FREEDOM    SIGNIFICANCE = 0.0857

SENTENCE LENGTH IN THREE NOVELS

**Figure 12.8**    SPSS analysis output for sentence length data

sorting data into rank order, and other commonly required types of manipulation. Its range of statistical facilities is wide, though not quite so comprehensive as that found in SPSS. For instance, the Wilcoxon signed-ranks test is not available, though the Mann–Whitney test is included. A simple guide to Minitab can be found in Ryan, Joiner and Ryan (1976).

Figure 12.9 shows a set of Minitab commands and data for the production of a frequency distribution and descriptive statistics for the language test data analysed in our first SPSS example. The command SET THE FOLLOWING INTO C1 simply reads the set of 30 scores, supplied in free format in a list following the instruction, and sets them into a column which can later be referred to as C1. The remaining commands request the mean, standard deviation and median (the mode and range are not available), and finally a histogram of the data. The output is shown in figure

```
SET THE FOLLOWING INTO C1
15 12 11 18 15 15 9 19 14 13 11 12 18 15 16 14 16 17 15 17 13 14 13 15 17
19 17 18 16 14
AVERAGE OF C1
STANDARD DEVIATION OF C1
MEDIAN OF C1
HISTOGRAM OF C1
STOP
```

**Figure 12.9    Minitab commands and data for analysis of language test scores**

```
− −  SET THE FOLLOWING INTO C1
COLUMN        C1
COUNT        30
            15.          12.          11.          18. . . .

− −  AVERAGE OF C1
      AVERAGE = 14.933

− −  STANDARD DEVIATION OF C1
      ST. DEV. =    2.4904

− −  MEDIAN OF C1
      MEDIAN =   15.000

− −  HISTOGRAM OF C1

  C1

    MIDDLE OF        NUMBER OF
    INTERVAL        OBSERVATIONS
        9.              1        *
       10.              0
       11.              2        **
       12.              2        **
       13.              3        ***
       14.              4        ****
       15.              6        ******
       16.              3        ***
       17.              4        ****
       18.              3        ***
       19.              2        **

− −  STOP
```

**Figure 12.10    Minitab analysis output for language test data**

12.10. Note that Minitab produces a sideways-on histogram consisting of a number of asterisks proportional to the frequency in each class.

In figure 12.11 is shown a file of commands and data for performing the $t$-test on sentence recall data, discussed earlier in relation to SPSS. The two sets of scores are set into two columns,

```
SET INTO C1
18   15   13   17   14   8   10   11   7   17
SET INTO C2
13   14   12   6   11   13   17   16   5
POOLED T FOR DATA IN C1 AND C2
STOP
```

Figure 12.11    Minitab commands and data for *t*-test on sentence recall

```
- - SET INTO C1
COLUMN          C1
COUNT           10
          18.              15.              13.              17. . . .

- - SET INTO C2
COLUMN          C2
COUNT            9
          13.              14.              12.               6. . . .

- - POOLED T FOR DATA IN C1 AND C2
    C1            N = 10        MEAN = 13.000        ST. DEV. = 3.89
    C2            N =  9        MEAN = 11.889        ST. DEV. = 4.08

DEGREES OF FREEDOM = 17

A 95.00 PERCENT C.I. FOR MU1–MU2 IS (  –2.7452,   4.9674)

TEST OF MU1 = MU2 VS. MU1 N.E. MU2
T = 0.608
THE TEST IS SIGNIFICANT AT 0.5512
CANNOT REJECT AT ALPHA = 0.05

- - STOP
```

Figure 12.12    Minitab analysis output for *t*-test on sentence recall

C1 and C2, and a *t*-test based on a pooled variance estimate is requested. The output (figure 12.12) gives the number of scores, mean and standard deviation, for each group, the number of degrees of freedom involved, the 95 per cent confidence interval for the difference between the means, the value of $t$, the probability of attaining such a value, and the conclusion to be drawn in a test at the 5 per cent level.

Finally, let us consider how, using Minitab, we might construct a contingency table and calculate chi-square for the data on sentence length in three novels, discussed earlier. The file of commands and data is shown in figure 12.13. The package is instructed to read the data into a three-column table, and then to perform

```
READ THE TABLE INTO C1, C2, C3
103   82   110
281  262  276
116  145  124
CHISQUARE ANALYSIS ON TABLE IN C1, C2, C3
STOP
```

**Figure 12.13**   Minitab commands and data for cross-tabulation and chi-square analysis of sentence length in three novels

```
− −  READ THE TABLE INTO C1, C2, C3
COLUMN          C1              C2              C3
COUNT           3               3               3
ROW
  1             103.            82.             110.
  2             281.            262.            276.
  3             116.            145.            124.

− −  CHISQUARE ANALYSIS ON TABLE IN C1, C2, C3
```

EXPECTED FREQUENCIES ARE PRINTED BELOW OBSERVED FREQUENCIES

|        | C1    | C2    | C3    | TOTALS |
|--------|-------|-------|-------|--------|
| 1      | 103   | 82    | 110   | 295    |
|        | 98.4  | 96.2  | 100.4 |        |
| 2      | 281   | 262   | 276   | 819    |
|        | 273.2 | 267.2 | 278.6 |        |
| 3      | 116   | 145   | 124   | 385    |
|        | 128.4 | 125.6 | 131.0 |        |
| TOTALS | 500   | 489   | 510   | 1499   |

TOTAL CHI SQUARE =

```
0.22 + 2.11 + 0.92 +
0.22 + 0.10 + 0.03 +
1.20 + 3.00 + 0.37 +

    = 8.17
```

DEGREES OF FREEDOM = $(3 - 1) \times (3 - 1) = 4$

− −  STOP

**Figure 12.14**   Minitab analysis output for sentence length data

a chi-square analysis. The output (figure 12.14) shows the contingency table, the contribution to chi-square made by each cell in the table, and the total chi-square, but, curiously, no figure for the probability associated with this value, which must be looked up in tables by the user.

## 12.4    The use of electronic calculators in statistical work

The student or researcher who has no access to a statistical package, and who is himself unable to program the computer to perform the statistical analyses he requires, can still benefit considerably from electronic aids. The wide range of quite inexpensive pocket

**Table 12.1    The use of a calculator to compute a mean and standard deviation**

| Figure entered | Function button(s) depressed | Screen display after depression of function button |
|---|---|---|
| 15 | $\Sigma+$ | 1. |
| 12 | $\Sigma+$ | 2. |
| 11 | $\Sigma+$ | 3. |
| 18 | $\Sigma+$ | 4. |
| 15 | $\Sigma+$ | 5. |
| 15 | $\Sigma+$ | 6. |
| 9 | $\Sigma+$ | 7. |
| 19 | $\Sigma+$ | 8. |
| 14 | $\Sigma+$ | 9. |
| 13 | $\Sigma+$ | 10. |
| 11 | $\Sigma+$ | 11. |
| 12 | $\Sigma+$ | 12. |
| 18 | $\Sigma+$ | 13. |
| 15 | $\Sigma+$ | 14. |
| 16 | $\Sigma+$ | 15. |
| 14 | $\Sigma+$ | 16. |
| 16 | $\Sigma+$ | 17. |
| 17 | $\Sigma+$ | 18. |
| 15 | $\Sigma+$ | 19. |
| 17 | $\Sigma+$ | 20. |
| 13 | $\Sigma+$ | 21. |
| 14 | $\Sigma+$ | 22. |
| 13 | $\Sigma+$ | 23. |
| 15 | $\Sigma+$ | 24. |
| 17 | $\Sigma+$ | 25. |
| 19 | $\Sigma+$ | 26. |
| 17 | $\Sigma+$ | 27. |
| 18 | $\Sigma+$ | 28. |
| 16 | $\Sigma+$ | 29. |
| 14 | $\Sigma+$ | 30. |
| | 2nd mean | 14.933 333 |
| | 2nd st. dev. | 2.490 441 5 |

calculators now available includes models with built-in statistical functions, or even with limited facilities for programming. Even models which do not have built-in functions will usually allow intermediate storage of results in the calculator's memory, thereby facilitating, for example, the accumulation of sums of squares, as well as sums of individual scores, in the calculation of a standard deviation.

One popular and inexpensive model of calculator has facilities for the automatic computation of the mean, standard deviation and variance of a set of data, also the Pearson correlation coefficient for two sets of scores. In table 12.1 is shown the sequence of operations for calculating the mean and standard deviation of the 30 language test scores processed earlier by means of SPSS and Minitab.

## 12.5   A final caveat

There is, of course, every reason why we should take advantage of computers or pocket calculators to reduce the tedium and the likelihood of error involved in calculating statistics from first principles. However, it cannot be too strongly emphasised that it is essential to understand the principles on which the calculation and use of the statistics are based. The competent scholar will have the knowledge to decide when a particular descriptive statistic or test is the most appropriate one to use, and will be thoroughly conversant with the limitations, as well as the advantages, of the procedures he adopts. It is hoped that this book will help to increase the level of awareness and understanding of statistics among that varied group of scholars whose interest is in the analysis of language.

# Appendix 1   Statistical tables

## Table A1    Random digits

| | | | | | | | | | |
|---|---|---|---|---|---|---|---|---|---|
| 49487 | 52802 | 28667 | 62058 | 87822 | 14704 | 18519 | 17889 | 45869 | 14454 |
| 29480 | 91539 | 46317 | 84803 | 86056 | 62812 | 33584 | 70391 | 77749 | 64906 |
| 25252 | 97738 | 23901 | 11106 | 86864 | 55808 | 22557 | 23214 | 15021 | 54268 |
| 02431 | 42193 | 96960 | 19620 | 29188 | 05863 | 92900 | 06836 | 13433 | 21709 |
| 69414 | 89353 | 70724 | 67893 | 23218 | 72452 | 03095 | 68333 | 13751 | 37260 |
| | | | | | | | | | |
| 77285 | 35179 | 92042 | 67581 | 67673 | 68374 | 71115 | 98166 | 43352 | 06414 |
| 52852 | 11444 | 71863 | 34534 | 69124 | 02760 | 06406 | 95234 | 87995 | 79560 |
| 98740 | 98054 | 30195 | 09891 | 18453 | 79464 | 01156 | 95522 | 06884 | 55073 |
| 85022 | 58736 | 12138 | 35146 | 62085 | 36170 | 25433 | 80787 | 96496 | 40579 |
| 17778 | 03840 | 21636 | 56269 | 08149 | 19001 | 67367 | 13138 | 02400 | 89515 |
| | | | | | | | | | |
| 81833 | 93449 | 57781 | 94621 | 90998 | 37561 | 59688 | 93299 | 27726 | 82167 |
| 63789 | 54958 | 33167 | 10909 | 40343 | 81023 | 61590 | 44474 | 39810 | 10305 |
| 61640 | 81740 | 60986 | 12498 | 71546 | 42249 | 13812 | 59902 | 27864 | 21809 |
| 42243 | 10153 | 20891 | 90883 | 15782 | 98167 | 86837 | 99166 | 92143 | 82441 |
| 45236 | 09129 | 53031 | 12260 | 01278 | 14404 | 40969 | 33419 | 14188 | 69557 |
| | | | | | | | | | |
| 40338 | 42477 | 78804 | 36272 | 72053 | 07958 | 67158 | 60979 | 79891 | 92409 |
| 54040 | 71253 | 88789 | 98203 | 54999 | 96564 | 00789 | 68879 | 47134 | 83941 |
| 49158 | 20908 | 44859 | 29089 | 76130 | 51442 | 34453 | 98590 | 37353 | 61137 |
| 80958 | 03808 | 83655 | 18415 | 96563 | 43582 | 82207 | 53322 | 30419 | 64435 |
| 07636 | 04876 | 61063 | 57571 | 69434 | 14965 | 20911 | 73162 | 33576 | 52839 |
| | | | | | | | | | |
| 37227 | 80750 | 08261 | 97048 | 60438 | 75053 | 05939 | 34414 | 16685 | 32103 |
| 99460 | 45915 | 45637 | 41353 | 35335 | 69087 | 57536 | 68418 | 10247 | 93253 |
| 60248 | 75845 | 37296 | 33783 | 42393 | 28185 | 31880 | 00241 | 31642 | 37526 |
| 95076 | 79089 | 87380 | 28982 | 97750 | 82221 | 35584 | 27444 | 85793 | 69755 |
| 20944 | 97852 | 26586 | 32796 | 51513 | 47475 | 48621 | 20067 | 88975 | 39506 |
| | | | | | | | | | |
| 30458 | 49207 | 62358 | 41532 | 30057 | 53017 | 10375 | 97204 | 98675 | 77634 |
| 38905 | 91282 | 79309 | 49022 | 17405 | 18830 | 09186 | 07629 | 01785 | 78317 |
| 96545 | 15638 | 90114 | 93730 | 13741 | 70177 | 49175 | 42113 | 21600 | 69625 |
| 21944 | 28328 | 00692 | 89164 | 96025 | 01383 | 50252 | 67044 | 70596 | 58266 |
| 36910 | 71928 | 63327 | 00980 | 32154 | 46006 | 62289 | 28079 | 03076 | 15619 |
| | | | | | | | | | |
| 48745 | 47626 | 28856 | 28382 | 60639 | 51370 | 70091 | 58261 | 70135 | 88259 |
| 32519 | 91993 | 59374 | 83994 | 59873 | 51217 | 62806 | 20028 | 26545 | 16820 |
| 75757 | 12965 | 29285 | 11481 | 31744 | 41754 | 24428 | 81819 | 02354 | 37895 |
| 07911 | 97756 | 89561 | 27464 | 25133 | 50026 | 16436 | 75846 | 83718 | 08533 |
| 89887 | 03328 | 76911 | 93168 | 56236 | 39056 | 67905 | 94933 | 05456 | 52347 |
| | | | | | | | | | |
| 30543 | 99488 | 75363 | 94187 | 32885 | 23887 | 10872 | 22793 | 26232 | 87356 |
| 68442 | 55201 | 33946 | 42495 | 28384 | 89889 | 50278 | 91985 | 58185 | 19124 |
| 22403 | 56698 | 88524 | 13692 | 55012 | 25343 | 76391 | 48029 | 72278 | 58586 |
| 70701 | 36907 | 51242 | 52083 | 43126 | 90379 | 60380 | 98513 | 85596 | 16528 |
| 69804 | 96122 | 42342 | 28467 | 79037 | 13218 | 63510 | 09071 | 52438 | 25840 |
| | | | | | | | | | |
| 65806 | 22398 | 19470 | 63653 | 27055 | 02606 | 43347 | 65384 | 02613 | 81668 |
| 43902 | 53070 | 54319 | 19347 | 59506 | 75440 | 90826 | 53652 | 92382 | 67623 |
| 49145 | 71587 | 14273 | 62440 | 15770 | 03281 | 58124 | 09533 | 43722 | 03856 |
| 47363 | 36295 | 62126 | 42358 | 20322 | 82000 | 52830 | 93540 | 13284 | 96496 |
| 26244 | 87033 | 90247 | 79131 | 38773 | 67687 | 45541 | 54976 | 17508 | 18367 |
| | | | | | | | | | |
| 72875 | 39496 | 06385 | 48458 | 30545 | 74383 | 22814 | 36752 | 10707 | 48774 |
| 09065 | 16283 | 61398 | 08288 | 00708 | 21816 | 39615 | 03102 | 02834 | 04116 |
| 68256 | 51225 | 92645 | 77747 | 33104 | 81206 | 00112 | 53445 | 04212 | 58476 |
| 38744 | 81018 | 41909 | 70458 | 72459 | 66136 | 97266 | 26490 | 10877 | 45022 |
| 44375 | 19619 | 35750 | 59924 | 82429 | 90288 | 61064 | 26489 | 87001 | 84273 |

Table A1 (continued)

| | | | | | | | | | |
|---|---|---|---|---|---|---|---|---|---|
| 57780 | 97609 | 52482 | 12783 | 88768 | 12323 | 64967 | 22970 | 11204 | 37576 |
| 68327 | 00067 | 17487 | 49149 | 25894 | 23639 | 86557 | 04139 | 10756 | 76285 |
| 55888 | 82253 | 67464 | 91628 | 88764 | 43598 | 45481 | 00331 | 15900 | 97699 |
| 84910 | 44827 | 31173 | 44247 | 56573 | 91759 | 79931 | 26644 | 27048 | 53704 |
| 35654 | 53638 | 00563 | 57230 | 07395 | 10813 | 99194 | 81592 | 96834 | 21374 |
| 46381 | 60071 | 20835 | 43110 | 31842 | 02855 | 73446 | 24456 | 24268 | 85291 |
| 11212 | 06034 | 77313 | 66896 | 47902 | 63483 | 09924 | 83635 | 30013 | 61791 |
| 49703 | 07226 | 73337 | 49223 | 73312 | 09534 | 64005 | 79267 | 76590 | 26066 |
| 05482 | 30340 | 24606 | 99042 | 16536 | 14267 | 84084 | 16198 | 94852 | 44305 |
| 92947 | 65090 | 47455 | 90675 | 89921 | 13036 | 92867 | 04786 | 76776 | 18675 |
| 51806 | 61445 | 32437 | 01129 | 03644 | 70024 | 07629 | 55805 | 85616 | 59569 |
| 16383 | 30577 | 91319 | 67998 | 72423 | 81307 | 75192 | 80443 | 09651 | 30068 |
| 30893 | 85406 | 42369 | 71836 | 74479 | 68273 | 78133 | 34506 | 68711 | 58725 |
| 59790 | 11682 | 63156 | 10443 | 99033 | 76460 | 36814 | 36917 | 37232 | 66218 |
| 06271 | 74980 | 46094 | 21881 | 43525 | 16516 | 26393 | 89082 | 24343 | 57546 |
| 93325 | 61834 | 40763 | 81178 | 17507 | 90432 | 50973 | 35591 | 36930 | 03184 |
| 46690 | 08927 | 32962 | 24882 | 83156 | 58597 | 88267 | 32479 | 80440 | 41668 |
| 82041 | 88942 | 57572 | 34539 | 43812 | 58483 | 43779 | 42718 | 46798 | 49079 |
| 14306 | 04003 | 91186 | 70093 | 62700 | 99408 | 72236 | 52722 | 37531 | 24590 |
| 63471 | 77583 | 80056 | 59027 | 37031 | 05819 | 90836 | 19530 | 07138 | 36431 |
| 68467 | 17634 | 84211 | 31776 | 92996 | 75644 | 82043 | 84157 | 10877 | 12536 |
| 94308 | 57895 | 08121 | 07088 | 65080 | 51928 | 74237 | 00449 | 86625 | 06626 |
| 52218 | 32502 | 82195 | 43867 | 79935 | 34620 | 37386 | 00243 | 46353 | 44499 |
| 46586 | 08309 | 52702 | 85464 | 06670 | 18796 | 74713 | 81632 | 34056 | 56461 |
| 07869 | 80471 | 69139 | 82408 | 33989 | 44250 | 79597 | 15182 | 14956 | 70423 |
| 46719 | 60281 | 88638 | 26909 | 32415 | 31864 | 53708 | 60219 | 44482 | 40004 |
| 74687 | 71227 | 59716 | 80619 | 56816 | 73807 | 94150 | 21991 | 22901 | 74351 |
| 42731 | 50249 | 11685 | 54034 | 12710 | 35159 | 00214 | 19440 | 61539 | 25717 |
| 71740 | 29429 | 86822 | 01187 | 96497 | 25823 | 18415 | 06087 | 05886 | 11205 |
| 96746 | 05938 | 11828 | 47727 | 02522 | 33147 | 92846 | 15010 | 96725 | 67903 |
| 27564 | 81744 | 51909 | 36192 | 45263 | 33212 | 71808 | 24753 | 72644 | 74441 |
| 21895 | 29683 | 26533 | 14740 | 94286 | 90342 | 24674 | 52762 | 22051 | 31743 |
| 01492 | 40778 | 05988 | 65760 | 13468 | 31132 | 37106 | 02723 | 40202 | 15824 |
| 55846 | 19271 | 22846 | 80425 | 00235 | 34292 | 72181 | 24910 | 25245 | 81239 |
| 14615 | 75196 | 40313 | 50783 | 66585 | 39010 | 76796 | 31385 | 26785 | 66830 |
| 77848 | 15755 | 91938 | 81915 | 65312 | 86956 | 26195 | 61525 | 97406 | 67988 |
| 87167 | 03106 | 52876 | 31670 | 23850 | 13257 | 77510 | 42393 | 53782 | 32412 |
| 73018 | 56511 | 89388 | 73133 | 12074 | 62538 | 57215 | 23476 | 92150 | 14737 |
| 29247 | 67792 | 10593 | 22772 | 03407 | 24319 | 19525 | 24672 | 21182 | 10765 |
| 17412 | 09161 | 34905 | 44524 | 20124 | 85151 | 25952 | 81930 | 43536 | 39705 |
| 68805 | 19830 | 87973 | 99691 | 25096 | 41497 | 57562 | 35553 | 77057 | 06161 |
| 40551 | 36740 | 61851 | 76158 | 35441 | 66188 | 87728 | 66375 | 98049 | 84604 |
| 90379 | 06314 | 21897 | 42800 | 63963 | 44258 | 14381 | 90884 | 66620 | 14538 |
| 09466 | 65311 | 95514 | 51559 | 29960 | 07521 | 42180 | 86677 | 94240 | 59783 |
| 15821 | 25078 | 19388 | 93798 | 50820 | 88254 | 20504 | 74158 | 35756 | 42100 |
| 10328 | 60890 | 05204 | 30069 | 79630 | 31572 | 63273 | 13703 | 52954 | 72793 |
| 49727 | 08160 | 81650 | 71690 | 56327 | 06729 | 22495 | 49756 | 43333 | 34533 |
| 71118 | 41798 | 34541 | 76432 | 40522 | 51521 | 74382 | 06305 | 11956 | 30611 |
| 53253 | 23100 | 03743 | 48999 | 37736 | 92186 | 19108 | 69017 | 21661 | 17175 |
| 12206 | 24205 | 32372 | 46438 | 67981 | 53226 | 24943 | 68659 | 91924 | 69555 |

# Table A2   The normal distribution

The table gives the proportion of the total area under the curve which lies beyond any given $z$ value (that is, the shaded area in the diagram). It is therefore appropriate for a one-tailed (directional) test. For a two-tailed (non-directional) test, the proportions must be doubled.

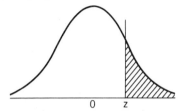

The figures down the left-hand side give values of $z$ to the first decimal place, and those across the top give the second decimal place.

| z | 0.00 | 0.01 | 0.02 | 0.03 | 0.04 | 0.05 | 0.06 | 0.07 | 0.08 | 0.09 |
|---|------|------|------|------|------|------|------|------|------|------|
| 0.0 | 0.5000 | 0.4960 | 0.4920 | 0.4880 | 0.4840 | 0.4801 | 0.4761 | 0.4721 | 0.4681 | 0.4641 |
| 0.1 | 0.4602 | 0.4562 | 0.4522 | 0.4483 | 0.4443 | 0.4404 | 0.4364 | 0.4325 | 0.4286 | 0.4247 |
| 0.2 | 0.4207 | 0.4168 | 0.4129 | 0.4090 | 0.4052 | 0.4013 | 0.3974 | 0.3936 | 0.3897 | 0.3859 |
| 0.3 | 0.3821 | 0.3783 | 0.3745 | 0.3707 | 0.3669 | 0.3632 | 0.3594 | 0.3557 | 0.3520 | 0.3483 |
| 0.4 | 0.3446 | 0.3409 | 0.3372 | 0.3336 | 0.3300 | 0.3264 | 0.3228 | 0.3192 | 0.3156 | 0.3121 |
| 0.5 | 0.3085 | 0.3050 | 0.3015 | 0.2981 | 0.2946 | 0.2912 | 0.2877 | 0.2843 | 0.2810 | 0.2776 |
| 0.6 | 0.2743 | 0.2709 | 0.2676 | 0.2643 | 0.2611 | 0.2578 | 0.2546 | 0.2514 | 0.2483 | 0.2451 |
| 0.7 | 0.2420 | 0.2389 | 0.2358 | 0.2327 | 0.2296 | 0.2266 | 0.2236 | 0.2206 | 0.2177 | 0.2148 |
| 0.8 | 0.2119 | 0.2090 | 0.2061 | 0.2033 | 0.2005 | 0.1977 | 0.1949 | 0.1922 | 0.1894 | 0.1867 |
| 0.9 | 0.1841 | 0.1814 | 0.1788 | 0.1762 | 0.1736 | 0.1711 | 0.1685 | 0.1660 | 0.1635 | 0.1611 |
| 1.0 | 0.1587 | 0.1562 | 0.1539 | 0.1515 | 0.1492 | 0.1469 | 0.1446 | 0.1423 | 0.1401 | 0.1379 |
| 1.1 | 0.1357 | 0.1335 | 0.1314 | 0.1292 | 0.1271 | 0.1251 | 0.1230 | 0.1210 | 0.1190 | 0.1170 |
| 1.2 | 0.1151 | 0.1131 | 0.1112 | 0.1093 | 0.1075 | 0.1056 | 0.1038 | 0.1020 | 0.1003 | 0.0985 |
| 1.3 | 0.0968 | 0.0951 | 0.0934 | 0.0918 | 0.0901 | 0.0885 | 0.0869 | 0.0853 | 0.0838 | 0.0823 |
| 1.4 | 0.0808 | 0.0793 | 0.0778 | 0.0764 | 0.0749 | 0.0735 | 0.0721 | 0.0708 | 0.0694 | 0.0681 |
| 1.5 | 0.0668 | 0.0655 | 0.0643 | 0.0630 | 0.0618 | 0.0606 | 0.0594 | 0.0582 | 0.0571 | 0.0559 |
| 1.6 | 0.0548 | 0.0537 | 0.0526 | 0.0516 | 0.0505 | 0.0495 | 0.0485 | 0.0475 | 0.0465 | 0.0455 |
| 1.7 | 0.0446 | 0.0436 | 0.0427 | 0.0418 | 0.0409 | 0.0401 | 0.0392 | 0.0384 | 0.0375 | 0.0367 |
| 1.8 | 0.0359 | 0.0351 | 0.0344 | 0.0336 | 0.0329 | 0.0322 | 0.0314 | 0.0307 | 0.0301 | 0.0294 |
| 1.9 | 0.0287 | 0.0281 | 0.0274 | 0.0268 | 0.0262 | 0.0256 | 0.0250 | 0.0244 | 0.0239 | 0.0233 |
| 2.0 | 0.0228 | 0.0222 | 0.0217 | 0.0212 | 0.0207 | 0.0202 | 0.0197 | 0.0192 | 0.0188 | 0.0183 |
| 2.1 | 0.0179 | 0.0174 | 0.0170 | 0.0166 | 0.0162 | 0.0158 | 0.0154 | 0.0150 | 0.0146 | 0.0143 |
| 2.2 | 0.0139 | 0.0136 | 0.0132 | 0.0129 | 0.0125 | 0.0122 | 0.0119 | 0.0116 | 0.0113 | 0.0110 |
| 2.3 | 0.0107 | 0.0104 | 0.0102 | 0.0099 | 0.0096 | 0.0094 | 0.0091 | 0.0089 | 0.0087 | 0.0084 |
| 2.4 | 0.0082 | 0.0080 | 0.0078 | 0.0075 | 0.0073 | 0.0071 | 0.0069 | 0.0068 | 0.0066 | 0.0064 |
| 2.5 | 0.0062 | 0.0060 | 0.0059 | 0.0057 | 0.0055 | 0.0054 | 0.0052 | 0.0051 | 0.0049 | 0.0048 |
| 2.6 | 0.0047 | 0.0045 | 0.0044 | 0.0043 | 0.0041 | 0.0040 | 0.0039 | 0.0038 | 0.0037 | 0.0036 |
| 2.7 | 0.0035 | 0.0034 | 0.0033 | 0.0032 | 0.0031 | 0.0030 | 0.0029 | 0.0028 | 0.0027 | 0.0026 |
| 2.8 | 0.0026 | 0.0025 | 0.0024 | 0.0023 | 0.0023 | 0.0022 | 0.0021 | 0.0021 | 0.0020 | 0.0019 |
| 2.9 | 0.0019 | 0.0018 | 0.0018 | 0.0017 | 0.0016 | 0.0016 | 0.0015 | 0.0015 | 0.0014 | 0.0014 |
| 3.0 | 0.0013 | 0.0013 | 0.0013 | 0.0012 | 0.0012 | 0.0011 | 0.0011 | 0.0011 | 0.0010 | 0.0010 |
| 3.1 | 0.0010 | 0.0009 | 0.0009 | 0.0009 | 0.0008 | 0.0008 | 0.0008 | 0.0008 | 0.0007 | 0.0007 |
| 3.2 | 0.0007 | 0.0007 | 0.0006 | 0.0006 | 0.0006 | 0.0006 | 0.0006 | 0.0005 | 0.0005 | 0.0005 |
| 3.3 | 0.0005 | 0.0005 | 0.0005 | 0.0004 | 0.0004 | 0.0004 | 0.0004 | 0.0004 | 0.0004 | 0.0003 |
| 3.4 | 0.0003 | 0.0003 | 0.0003 | 0.0003 | 0.0003 | 0.0003 | 0.0003 | 0.0003 | 0.0003 | 0.0002 |
| 3.5 | 0.0002 | 0.0002 | 0.0002 | 0.0002 | 0.0002 | 0.0002 | 0.0002 | 0.0002 | 0.0002 | 0.0002 |

## Table A3 The *t*-distribution

The table gives critical values of *t* for significance at various levels, in a two-tailed/non-directional or a one-tailed/directional test, for different numbers of degrees of freedom. These critical values are the values beyond which lies that proportion of the area under the curve which corresponds to the significance level.

| | Significance level: two-tailed/non-directional | | | | |
|---|---|---|---|---|---|
| | 0.20 | 0.10 | 0.05 | 0.02 | 0.01 |
| | Significance level: one-tailed/directional | | | | |
| Degrees of freedom | 0.10 | 0.05 | 0.025 | 0.01 | 0.005 |
| 1 | 3.078 | 6.314 | 12.71 | 31.82 | 63.66 |
| 2 | 1.886 | 2.920 | 4.303 | 6.965 | 9.925 |
| 3 | 1.638 | 2.353 | 3.182 | 4.541 | 5.841 |
| 4 | 1.533 | 2.132 | 2.776 | 3.747 | 4.604 |
| 5 | 1.476 | 2.015 | 2.571 | 3.365 | 4.032 |
| 6 | 1.440 | 1.943 | 2.447 | 3.143 | 3.707 |
| 7 | 1.415 | 1.895 | 2.365 | 2.998 | 3.499 |
| 8 | 1.397 | 1.860 | 2.306 | 2.896 | 3.355 |
| 9 | 1.383 | 1.833 | 2.262 | 2.821 | 3.250 |
| 10 | 1.372 | 1.812 | 2.228 | 2.764 | 3.169 |
| 11 | 1.363 | 1.796 | 2.201 | 2.718 | 3.106 |
| 12 | 1.356 | 1.782 | 2.179 | 2.681 | 3.055 |
| 13 | 1.350 | 1.771 | 2.160 | 2.650 | 3.012 |
| 14 | 1.345 | 1.761 | 2.145 | 2.624 | 2.977 |
| 15 | 1.341 | 1.753 | 2.131 | 2.602 | 2.947 |
| 16 | 1.337 | 1.746 | 2.120 | 2.583 | 2.921 |
| 17 | 1.333 | 1.740 | 2.110 | 2.567 | 2.898 |
| 18 | 1.330 | 1.734 | 2.101 | 2.552 | 2.878 |
| 19 | 1.328 | 1.729 | 2.093 | 2.539 | 2.861 |
| 20 | 1.325 | 1.725 | 2.086 | 2.528 | 2.845 |
| 21 | 1.323 | 1.721 | 2.080 | 2.518 | 2.831 |
| 22 | 1.321 | 1.717 | 2.074 | 2.508 | 2.819 |
| 23 | 1.319 | 1.714 | 2.069 | 2.500 | 2.807 |
| 24 | 1.318 | 1.711 | 2.064 | 2.492 | 2.797 |
| 25 | 1.316 | 1.708 | 2.060 | 2.485 | 2.787 |
| 26 | 1.315 | 1.706 | 2.056 | 2.479 | 2.779 |
| 27 | 1.314 | 1.703 | 2.052 | 2.473 | 2.771 |
| 28 | 1.313 | 1.701 | 2.048 | 2.467 | 2.763 |
| 29 | 1.311 | 1.699 | 2.045 | 2.462 | 2.756 |
| 30 | 1.310 | 1.697 | 2.042 | 2.457 | 2.750 |
| 40 | 1.303 | 1.684 | 2.021 | 2.423 | 2.704 |
| 60 | 1.296 | 1.671 | 2.000 | 2.390 | 2.660 |
| 120 | 1.289 | 1.658 | 1.980 | 2.358 | 2.617 |
| ∞ | 1.282 | 1.645 | 1.960 | 2.326 | 2.576 |

## Table A4  The Mann–Whitney $U$-test

The first table gives the critical values for significance at the $p \leqslant 0.05$ level in a two-tailed/non-directional test, and for the $p \leqslant 0.025$ level in a one-tailed/ directional test. The second table gives the critical values for the $p \leqslant 0.01$ level in a two-tailed/non-directional test, and for the $p \leqslant 0.005$ level in a one-tailed/directional test. For significance, the calculated value of $U$ must be *smaller than or equal to* the critical value. $N_1$ and $N_2$ are the number of observations in the smaller and larger group, respectively.

| | | | | | | $N_2$ | | | | | | | | | | |
|---|---|---|---|---|---|---|---|---|---|---|---|---|---|---|---|
| | 5 | 6 | 7 | 8 | 9 | 10 | 11 | 12 | 13 | 14 | 15 | 16 | 17 | 18 | 19 | 20 |

$N_1$

$p \leqslant 0.05$ (two-tailed), $p \leqslant 0.025$ (one-tailed)

| $N_1$ | 5 | 6 | 7 | 8 | 9 | 10 | 11 | 12 | 13 | 14 | 15 | 16 | 17 | 18 | 19 | 20 |
|---|---|---|---|---|---|---|---|---|---|---|---|---|---|---|---|---|
| 5 | 2 | 3 | 5 | 6 | 7 | 8 | 9 | 11 | 12 | 13 | 14 | 15 | 17 | 18 | 19 | 20 |
| 6 | | 5 | 6 | 8 | 10 | 11 | 13 | 14 | 16 | 17 | 19 | 21 | 22 | 24 | 25 | 27 |
| 7 | | | 8 | 10 | 12 | 14 | 16 | 18 | 20 | 22 | 24 | 26 | 28 | 30 | 32 | 34 |
| 8 | | | | 13 | 15 | 17 | 19 | 22 | 24 | 26 | 29 | 31 | 34 | 36 | 38 | 41 |
| 9 | | | | | 17 | 20 | 23 | 26 | 28 | 31 | 34 | 37 | 39 | 42 | 45 | 48 |
| 10 | | | | | | 23 | 26 | 29 | 33 | 36 | 39 | 42 | 45 | 48 | 52 | 55 |
| 11 | | | | | | | 30 | 33 | 37 | 40 | 44 | 47 | 51 | 55 | 58 | 62 |
| 12 | | | | | | | | 37 | 41 | 45 | 49 | 53 | 57 | 61 | 65 | 69 |
| 13 | | | | | | | | | 45 | 50 | 54 | 59 | 63 | 67 | 72 | 76 |
| 14 | | | | | | | | | | 55 | 59 | 64 | 69 | 74 | 78 | 83 |
| 15 | | | | | | | | | | | 64 | 70 | 75 | 80 | 85 | 90 |
| 16 | | | | | | | | | | | | 75 | 81 | 86 | 92 | 98 |
| 17 | | | | | | | | | | | | | 87 | 93 | 99 | 105 |
| 18 | | | | | | | | | | | | | | 99 | 106 | 112 |
| 19 | | | | | | | | | | | | | | | 113 | 119 |
| 20 | | | | | | | | | | | | | | | | 127 |

$p \leqslant 0.01$ (two-tailed), $p \leqslant 0.005$ (one-tailed)

| $N_1$ | 5 | 6 | 7 | 8 | 9 | 10 | 11 | 12 | 13 | 14 | 15 | 16 | 17 | 18 | 19 | 20 |
|---|---|---|---|---|---|---|---|---|---|---|---|---|---|---|---|---|
| 5 | 0 | 1 | 1 | 2 | 3 | 4 | 5 | 6 | 7 | 7 | 8 | 9 | 10 | 11 | 12 | 13 |
| 6 | | 2 | 3 | 4 | 5 | 6 | 7 | 9 | 10 | 11 | 12 | 13 | 15 | 16 | 17 | 18 |
| 7 | | | 4 | 6 | 7 | 9 | 10 | 12 | 13 | 15 | 16 | 18 | 19 | 21 | 22 | 24 |
| 8 | | | | 7 | 9 | 11 | 13 | 15 | 17 | 18 | 20 | 22 | 24 | 26 | 28 | 30 |
| 9 | | | | | 11 | 13 | 16 | 18 | 20 | 22 | 24 | 27 | 29 | 31 | 33 | 36 |
| 10 | | | | | | 16 | 18 | 21 | 24 | 26 | 29 | 31 | 34 | 37 | 39 | 42 |
| 11 | | | | | | | 21 | 24 | 27 | 30 | 33 | 36 | 39 | 42 | 45 | 48 |
| 12 | | | | | | | | 27 | 31 | 34 | 37 | 41 | 44 | 47 | 51 | 54 |
| 13 | | | | | | | | | 34 | 38 | 42 | 45 | 49 | 53 | 57 | 60 |
| 14 | | | | | | | | | | 42 | 46 | 50 | 54 | 58 | 63 | 67 |
| 15 | | | | | | | | | | | 51 | 55 | 60 | 64 | 69 | 73 |
| 16 | | | | | | | | | | | | 60 | 65 | 70 | 74 | 79 |
| 17 | | | | | | | | | | | | | 70 | 75 | 81 | 86 |
| 18 | | | | | | | | | | | | | | 81 | 87 | 92 |
| 19 | | | | | | | | | | | | | | | 93 | 99 |
| 20 | | | | | | | | | | | | | | | | 105 |

## Table A5    The Wilcoxon signed-ranks test

The table gives critical values of *W* for different values of *N* (the number of non-tied pairs of scores). For significance, the calculated value must be *smaller than or equal to* the critical value.

| | Significance level: two-tailed/non-directional | |
| | 0.05 | 0.01 |
| --- | --- | --- |
| | Significance level: one-tailed/directional | |
| N | 0.025 | 0.005 |
| 6 | 0 | – |
| 7 | 2 | – |
| 8 | 3 | 0 |
| 9 | 5 | 1 |
| 10 | 8 | 3 |
| 11 | 10 | 5 |
| 12 | 13 | 7 |
| 13 | 17 | 9 |
| 14 | 21 | 12 |
| 15 | 25 | 15 |
| 16 | 29 | 19 |
| 17 | 34 | 23 |
| 18 | 40 | 27 |
| 19 | 46 | 32 |
| 20 | 52 | 37 |
| 21 | 58 | 42 |
| 22 | 65 | 48 |
| 23 | 73 | 54 |
| 24 | 81 | 61 |
| 25 | 89 | 68 |

# Table A6   The sign test

The table gives critical values of $x$ (the number of cases with the less frequent
sign) for different values of $N$ (the number of non-tied pairs of scores). For
significance, the computed value of $x$ must be *smaller than or equal to* the
critical value.

| | Significance level: two-tailed/non-directional | | |
| | 0.10 | 0.05 | 0.02 |
| --- | --- | --- | --- |
| | | Significance level: one-tailed/directional | |
| N | 0.05 | 0.025 | 0.01 |
| 5 | 0 | — | — |
| 6 | 0 | 0 | — |
| 7 | 0 | 0 | 0 |
| 8 | 1 | 0 | 0 |
| 9 | 1 | 1 | 0 |
| 10 | 1 | 1 | 0 |
| 11 | 2 | 1 | 1 |
| 12 | 2 | 2 | 1 |
| 13 | 3 | 2 | 1 |
| 14 | 3 | 2 | 2 |
| 15 | 3 | 3 | 2 |
| 16 | 4 | 3 | 2 |
| 17 | 4 | 4 | 3 |
| 18 | 5 | 4 | 3 |
| 19 | 5 | 4 | 4 |
| 20 | 5 | 5 | 4 |
| 21 | 6 | 5 | 4 |
| 22 | 6 | 5 | 5 |
| 23 | 7 | 6 | 5 |
| 24 | 7 | 6 | 5 |
| 25 | 7 | 7 | 6 |

## Table A7    The chi-square distribution

The table gives the critical values of $\chi^2$ in a two-tailed/non-directional test, for different numbers of degrees of freedom (df). For significance, the calculated value must be *greater than or equal to* the critical value.

| df | Significance level | | | | | |
|---|---|---|---|---|---|---|
| | 0.20 | 0.10 | 0.05 | 0.025 | 0.01 | 0.001 |
| 1 | 1.64 | 2.71 | 3.84 | 5.02 | 6.64 | 10.83 |
| 2 | 3.22 | 4.61 | 5.99 | 7.38 | 9.21 | 13.82 |
| 3 | 4.64 | 6.25 | 7.82 | 9.35 | 11.34 | 16.27 |
| 4 | 5.99 | 7.78 | 9.49 | 11.14 | 13.28 | 18.47 |
| 5 | 7.29 | 9.24 | 11.07 | 12.83 | 15.09 | 20.52 |
| 6 | 8.56 | 10.64 | 12.59 | 14.45 | 16.81 | 22.46 |
| 7 | 9.80 | 12.02 | 14.07 | 16.01 | 18.48 | 24.32 |
| 8 | 11.03 | 13.36 | 15.51 | 17.53 | 20.09 | 26.12 |
| 9 | 12.24 | 14.68 | 16.92 | 19.02 | 21.67 | 27.88 |
| 10 | 13.44 | 15.99 | 18.31 | 20.48 | 23.21 | 29.59 |
| 11 | 14.63 | 17.28 | 19.68 | 21.92 | 24.72 | 31.26 |
| 12 | 15.81 | 18.55 | 21.03 | 23.34 | 26.22 | 32.91 |
| 13 | 16.98 | 19.81 | 22.36 | 24.74 | 27.69 | 34.53 |
| 14 | 18.15 | 21.06 | 23.68 | 26.12 | 29.14 | 36.12 |
| 15 | 19.31 | 22.31 | 25.00 | 27.49 | 30.58 | 37.70 |
| 16 | 20.47 | 23.54 | 26.30 | 28.85 | 32.00 | 39.25 |
| 17 | 21.61 | 24.77 | 27.59 | 30.19 | 33.41 | 40.79 |
| 18 | 22.76 | 25.99 | 28.87 | 31.53 | 34.81 | 42.31 |
| 19 | 23.90 | 27.20 | 30.14 | 32.85 | 36.19 | 43.82 |
| 20 | 25.04 | 28.41 | 31.41 | 34.17 | 37.57 | 45.31 |
| 21 | 26.17 | 29.62 | 32.67 | 35.48 | 38.93 | 46.80 |
| 22 | 27.30 | 30.81 | 33.92 | 36.78 | 40.29 | 48.27 |
| 23 | 28.43 | 32.01 | 35.17 | 38.08 | 41.64 | 49.73 |
| 24 | 29.55 | 33.20 | 36.42 | 39.36 | 42.98 | 51.18 |
| 25 | 30.68 | 34.38 | 37.65 | 40.65 | 44.31 | 52.62 |
| 26 | 31.79 | 35.56 | 38.89 | 41.92 | 45.64 | 54.05 |
| 27 | 32.91 | 36.74 | 40.11 | 43.19 | 46.96 | 55.48 |
| 28 | 34.03 | 37.92 | 41.34 | 44.46 | 48.28 | 56.89 |
| 29 | 35.14 | 39.09 | 42.56 | 45.72 | 49.59 | 58.30 |
| 30 | 36.25 | 40.26 | 43.77 | 46.98 | 50.89 | 59.70 |
| 40 | 47.27 | 51.81 | 55.76 | 59.34 | 63.69 | 73.40 |
| 50 | 58.16 | 63.17 | 67.50 | 71.42 | 76.15 | 86.66 |
| 60 | 68.97 | 74.40 | 79.08 | 83.30 | 88.38 | 99.61 |
| 70 | 79.71 | 85.53 | 90.53 | 95.02 | 100.4 | 112.3 |

# Table A8   The *F* distribution

The table gives the critical values of *F* for different numbers of degrees of freedom (df) in the numerator and in the denominator of the expression for *F*. For each entry, two values are given. The upper value is the critical value for the $p \leqslant 0.05$ level in a one-tailed/directional test, and for the $p \leqslant 0.10$ level in a two-tailed/non-directional test. The lower value is the critical value for the $p \leqslant 0.01$ level in a one-tailed/directional test and for the $p \leqslant 0.02$ level in a two-tailed/non-directional test.

| Df in denominator | \multicolumn{16}{c}{Df in numerator} |
|---|---|---|---|---|---|---|---|---|---|---|---|---|---|---|---|---|
| | 1 | 2 | 3 | 4 | 5 | 6 | 7 | 8 | 9 | 10 | 12 | 15 | 20 | 30 | 50 | ∞ |
| 1 | 161 | 200 | 216 | 225 | 230 | 234 | 237 | 239 | 241 | 242 | 244 | 246 | 248 | 250 | 252 | 254 |
|   | 4 052 | 5 000 | 5 403 | 5 625 | 5 764 | 5 859 | 5 928 | 5 981 | 6 022 | 6 056 | 6 106 | 6 157 | 6 209 | 6 261 | 6 303 | 6 366 |
| 2 | 18.5 | 19.0 | 19.2 | 19.2 | 19.3 | 19.3 | 19.4 | 19.4 | 19.4 | 19.4 | 19.4 | 19.4 | 19.4 | 19.5 | 19.5 | 19.5 |
|   | 98.5 | 99.0 | 99.2 | 99.2 | 99.3 | 99.3 | 99.4 | 99.4 | 99.4 | 99.4 | 99.4 | 99.4 | 99.4 | 99.5 | 99.5 | 99.5 |
| 3 | 10.1 | 9.55 | 9.28 | 9.12 | 9.01 | 8.94 | 8.89 | 8.85 | 8.81 | 8.79 | 8.74 | 8.70 | 8.66 | 8.62 | 8.58 | 8.53 |
|   | 34.1 | 30.8 | 29.5 | 28.7 | 28.2 | 27.9 | 27.7 | 27.5 | 27.3 | 27.2 | 27.1 | 26.9 | 26.7 | 26.5 | 26.4 | 26.1 |
| 4 | 7.71 | 6.94 | 6.59 | 6.39 | 6.26 | 6.16 | 6.09 | 6.04 | 6.00 | 5.96 | 5.91 | 5.86 | 5.80 | 5.75 | 5.70 | 5.63 |
|   | 21.2 | 18.0 | 16.7 | 16.0 | 15.5 | 15.2 | 15.0 | 14.8 | 14.7 | 14.5 | 14.4 | 14.2 | 14.0 | 13.8 | 13.7 | 13.5 |
| 5 | 6.61 | 5.79 | 5.41 | 5.19 | 5.05 | 4.95 | 4.88 | 4.82 | 4.77 | 4.74 | 4.68 | 4.62 | 4.56 | 4.50 | 4.44 | 4.36 |
|   | 16.3 | 13.3 | 12.1 | 11.4 | 11.0 | 10.7 | 10.5 | 10.3 | 10.2 | 10.1 | 9.89 | 9.72 | 9.55 | 9.38 | 9.24 | 9.02 |
| 6 | 5.99 | 5.14 | 4.76 | 4.53 | 4.39 | 4.28 | 4.21 | 4.15 | 4.10 | 4.06 | 4.00 | 3.94 | 3.87 | 3.81 | 3.75 | 3.67 |
|   | 13.7 | 10.9 | 9.78 | 9.15 | 8.75 | 8.47 | 8.26 | 8.10 | 7.98 | 7.87 | 7.72 | 7.56 | 7.40 | 7.23 | 7.09 | 6.88 |
| 7 | 5.59 | 4.74 | 4.35 | 4.12 | 3.97 | 3.87 | 3.79 | 3.73 | 3.68 | 3.64 | 3.57 | 3.51 | 3.44 | 3.38 | 3.32 | 3.23 |
|   | 12.2 | 9.55 | 8.45 | 7.85 | 7.46 | 7.19 | 6.99 | 6.84 | 6.72 | 6.62 | 6.47 | 6.31 | 6.16 | 5.99 | 5.86 | 5.65 |

**Table A8** (continued)

| Df in denominator | Df in numerator | | | | | | | | | | | | | | | |
|---|---|---|---|---|---|---|---|---|---|---|---|---|---|---|---|---|
| | 1 | 2 | 3 | 4 | 5 | 6 | 7 | 8 | 9 | 10 | 12 | 15 | 20 | 30 | 50 | ∞ |
| 8 | 5.32 / 11.3 | 4.46 / 8.65 | 4.07 / 7.59 | 3.84 / 7.01 | 3.69 / 6.63 | 3.58 / 6.37 | 3.50 / 6.18 | 3.44 / 6.03 | 3.39 / 5.91 | 3.35 / 5.81 | 3.28 / 5.67 | 3.22 / 5.52 | 3.15 / 5.36 | 3.08 / 5.20 | 3.02 / 5.07 | 2.93 / 4.86 |
| 9 | 5.12 / 10.6 | 4.26 / 8.02 | 3.86 / 6.99 | 3.63 / 6.42 | 3.48 / 6.06 | 3.37 / 5.80 | 3.29 / 5.61 | 3.23 / 5.47 | 3.18 / 5.35 | 3.14 / 5.26 | 3.07 / 5.11 | 3.01 / 4.96 | 2.94 / 4.81 | 2.86 / 4.65 | 2.80 / 4.52 | 2.71 / 4.31 |
| 10 | 4.96 / 10.0 | 4.10 / 7.56 | 3.71 / 6.55 | 3.48 / 5.99 | 3.33 / 5.64 | 3.22 / 5.39 | 3.14 / 5.20 | 3.07 / 5.06 | 3.02 / 4.94 | 2.98 / 4.85 | 2.91 / 4.71 | 2.85 / 4.56 | 2.77 / 4.41 | 2.70 / 4.25 | 2.64 / 4.12 | 2.54 / 3.91 |
| 11 | 4.84 / 9.65 | 3.98 / 7.21 | 3.59 / 6.22 | 3.36 / 5.67 | 3.20 / 5.32 | 3.09 / 5.07 | 3.01 / 4.89 | 2.95 / 4.74 | 2.90 / 4.63 | 2.85 / 4.54 | 2.79 / 4.40 | 2.72 / 4.25 | 2.65 / 4.10 | 2.57 / 3.94 | 2.51 / 3.81 | 2.40 / 3.60 |
| 12 | 4.75 / 9.33 | 3.89 / 6.93 | 3.49 / 5.95 | 3.26 / 5.41 | 3.11 / 5.06 | 3.00 / 4.82 | 2.91 / 4.64 | 2.85 / 4.50 | 2.80 / 4.39 | 2.75 / 4.30 | 2.69 / 4.16 | 2.62 / 4.01 | 2.54 / 3.86 | 2.47 / 3.70 | 2.40 / 3.57 | 2.30 / 3.36 |
| 13 | 4.67 / 9.07 | 3.81 / 6.70 | 3.41 / 5.74 | 3.18 / 5.21 | 3.03 / 4.86 | 2.92 / 4.62 | 2.83 / 4.44 | 2.77 / 4.30 | 2.71 / 4.19 | 2.67 / 4.10 | 2.60 / 3.96 | 2.53 / 3.82 | 2.46 / 3.66 | 2.38 / 3.51 | 2.31 / 3.38 | 2.21 / 3.17 |
| 14 | 4.60 / 8.86 | 3.74 / 6.51 | 3.34 / 5.56 | 3.11 / 5.04 | 2.96 / 4.69 | 2.85 / 4.46 | 2.76 / 4.28 | 2.70 / 4.14 | 2.65 / 4.03 | 2.60 / 3.94 | 2.53 / 3.80 | 2.46 / 3.66 | 2.39 / 3.51 | 2.31 / 3.35 | 2.24 / 3.22 | 2.13 / 3.00 |
| 15 | 4.54 / 8.68 | 3.68 / 6.36 | 3.29 / 5.42 | 3.06 / 4.89 | 2.90 / 4.56 | 2.79 / 4.32 | 2.71 / 4.14 | 2.64 / 4.00 | 2.59 / 3.89 | 2.54 / 3.80 | 2.48 / 3.67 | 2.40 / 3.52 | 2.33 / 3.37 | 2.25 / 3.21 | 2.18 / 3.08 | 2.07 / 2.87 |
| 16 | 4.49 / 8.53 | 3.63 / 6.23 | 3.24 / 5.29 | 3.01 / 4.77 | 2.85 / 4.44 | 2.74 / 4.20 | 2.66 / 4.03 | 2.59 / 3.89 | 2.54 / 3.78 | 2.49 / 3.69 | 2.42 / 3.55 | 2.35 / 3.41 | 2.28 / 3.26 | 2.19 / 3.10 | 2.12 / 2.97 | 2.01 / 2.75 |
| 17 | 4.45 / 8.40 | 3.59 / 6.11 | 3.20 / 5.18 | 2.96 / 4.67 | 2.81 / 4.34 | 2.70 / 4.10 | 2.61 / 3.93 | 2.55 / 3.79 | 2.49 / 3.68 | 2.45 / 3.59 | 2.38 / 3.46 | 2.31 / 3.31 | 2.23 / 3.16 | 2.15 / 3.00 | 2.08 / 2.87 | 1.96 / 2.65 |
| 18 | 4.41 / | 3.55 / | 3.16 / | 2.93 / | 2.77 / | 2.66 / | 2.58 / | 2.51 / | 2.46 / | 2.41 / | 2.34 / | 2.27 / | 2.19 / | 2.11 / | 2.04 / | 1.92 / |

| | 8.18 | 5.93 | 5.01 | 4.50 | 4.17 | 3.94 | 3.77 | 3.63 | 3.52 | 3.43 | 3.30 | 3.15 | 3.00 | 2.84 | 2.71 | 2.49 |
|---|---|---|---|---|---|---|---|---|---|---|---|---|---|---|---|---|
| 20 | 4.35 / 8.10 | 3.49 / 5.85 | 3.10 / 4.94 | 2.87 / 4.43 | 2.71 / 4.10 | 2.60 / 3.87 | 2.51 / 3.70 | 2.45 / 3.56 | 2.39 / 3.46 | 2.35 / 3.37 | 2.28 / 3.23 | 2.20 / 3.09 | 2.12 / 2.94 | 2.04 / 2.78 | 1.97 / 2.64 | 1.84 / 2.42 |
| 25 | 4.24 / 7.77 | 3.39 / 5.57 | 2.99 / 4.68 | 2.76 / 4.18 | 2.60 / 3.85 | 2.49 / 3.63 | 2.40 / 3.46 | 2.34 / 3.32 | 2.28 / 3.22 | 2.24 / 3.13 | 2.16 / 2.99 | 2.09 / 2.85 | 2.01 / 2.70 | 1.92 / 2.54 | 1.84 / 2.40 | 1.71 / 2.17 |
| 30 | 4.17 / 7.56 | 3.32 / 5.39 | 2.92 / 4.51 | 2.69 / 4.02 | 2.53 / 3.70 | 2.42 / 3.47 | 2.33 / 3.30 | 2.27 / 3.17 | 2.21 / 3.07 | 2.16 / 2.98 | 2.09 / 2.84 | 2.01 / 2.70 | 1.93 / 2.55 | 1.84 / 2.39 | 1.76 / 2.25 | 1.62 / 2.01 |
| 35 | 4.12 / 7.42 | 3.27 / 5.27 | 2.87 / 4.40 | 2.64 / 3.91 | 2.49 / 3.59 | 2.37 / 3.37 | 2.29 / 3.20 | 2.22 / 3.07 | 2.16 / 2.96 | 2.11 / 2.88 | 2.04 / 2.74 | 1.96 / 2.60 | 1.88 / 2.44 | 1.79 / 2.28 | 1.70 / 2.14 | 1.56 / 1.89 |
| 40 | 4.08 / 7.31 | 3.23 / 5.18 | 2.84 / 4.31 | 2.61 / 3.83 | 2.45 / 3.51 | 2.34 / 3.29 | 2.25 / 3.12 | 2.18 / 2.99 | 2.12 / 2.89 | 2.08 / 2.80 | 2.00 / 2.66 | 1.92 / 2.52 | 1.84 / 2.37 | 1.74 / 2.20 | 1.66 / 2.06 | 1.51 / 1.80 |
| 45 | 4.06 / 7.23 | 3.20 / 5.11 | 2.81 / 4.25 | 2.58 / 3.77 | 2.42 / 3.45 | 2.31 / 3.23 | 2.22 / 3.07 | 2.15 / 2.94 | 2.10 / 2.83 | 2.05 / 2.74 | 1.97 / 2.61 | 1.89 / 2.46 | 1.81 / 2.31 | 1.71 / 2.14 | 1.63 / 2.00 | 1.47 / 1.74 |
| 50 | 4.03 / 7.17 | 3.18 / 5.06 | 2.79 / 4.20 | 2.56 / 3.72 | 2.40 / 3.41 | 2.29 / 3.19 | 2.20 / 3.02 | 2.13 / 2.89 | 2.07 / 2.78 | 2.03 / 2.70 | 1.95 / 2.56 | 1.87 / 2.42 | 1.78 / 2.27 | 1.69 / 2.10 | 1.60 / 1.95 | 1.44 / 1.68 |
| 60 | 4.00 / 7.08 | 3.15 / 4.98 | 2.76 / 4.13 | 2.53 / 3.65 | 2.37 / 3.34 | 2.25 / 3.12 | 2.17 / 2.95 | 2.10 / 2.82 | 2.04 / 2.72 | 1.99 / 2.63 | 1.92 / 2.50 | 1.84 / 2.35 | 1.75 / 2.20 | 1.65 / 2.03 | 1.56 / 1.88 | 1.39 / 1.60 |
| 80 | 3.96 / 6.96 | 3.11 / 4.88 | 2.72 / 4.04 | 2.49 / 3.56 | 2.33 / 3.26 | 2.21 / 3.04 | 2.13 / 2.87 | 2.06 / 2.74 | 2.00 / 2.64 | 1.95 / 2.55 | 1.88 / 2.42 | 1.79 / 2.27 | 1.70 / 2.12 | 1.60 / 1.94 | 1.51 / 1.79 | 1.32 / 1.49 |
| 100 | 3.94 / 6.90 | 3.09 / 4.82 | 2.70 / 3.98 | 2.46 / 3.51 | 2.31 / 3.21 | 2.19 / 2.99 | 2.10 / 2.82 | 2.03 / 2.69 | 1.97 / 2.59 | 1.93 / 2.50 | 1.85 / 2.37 | 1.77 / 2.22 | 1.68 / 2.07 | 1.57 / 1.89 | 1.48 / 1.74 | 1.28 / 1.43 |
| 120 | 3.92 / 6.85 | 3.07 / 4.79 | 2.68 / 3.95 | 2.45 / 3.48 | 2.29 / 3.17 | 2.18 / 2.96 | 2.09 / 2.79 | 2.02 / 2.66 | 1.96 / 2.56 | 1.91 / 2.47 | 1.83 / 2.34 | 1.75 / 2.19 | 1.66 / 2.03 | 1.55 / 1.86 | 1.46 / 1.70 | 1.25 / 1.38 |
| ∞ | 3.84 / 6.63 | 3.00 / 4.61 | 2.60 / 3.78 | 2.37 / 3.32 | 2.21 / 3.02 | 2.10 / 2.80 | 2.01 / 2.64 | 1.94 / 2.51 | 1.88 / 2.41 | 1.83 / 2.32 | 1.75 / 2.18 | 1.67 / 2.04 | 1.57 / 1.88 | 1.46 / 1.70 | 1.35 / 1.52 | 1.00 / 1.00 |

## Table A9    The Pearson product–moment correlation coefficient

The table gives the critical values of the Pearson product–moment correlation coefficient, $r$, for different numbers of pairs of observations, $N$. For significance, the calculated value of $r$ must be *greater than or equal to* the critical value.

| | Significance level: two-tailed/non-directional | | | |
|---|---|---|---|---|
| | 0.20 | 0.10 | 0.05 | 0.01 |
| | Significance level: one-tailed/directional | | | |
| N | 0.10 | 0.05 | 0.025 | 0.005 |
| 3 | 0.951 | 0.988 | 0.997 | 1.000 |
| 4 | 0.800 | 0.900 | 0.950 | 0.990 |
| 5 | 0.687 | 0.805 | 0.878 | 0.959 |
| 6 | 0.608 | 0.729 | 0.811 | 0.917 |
| 7 | 0.551 | 0.669 | 0.754 | 0.875 |
| 8 | 0.507 | 0.621 | 0.707 | 0.834 |
| 9 | 0.472 | 0.582 | 0.666 | 0.798 |
| 10 | 0.443 | 0.549 | 0.632 | 0.765 |
| 11 | 0.419 | 0.521 | 0.602 | 0.735 |
| 12 | 0.398 | 0.497 | 0.576 | 0.708 |
| 13 | 0.380 | 0.476 | 0.553 | 0.684 |
| 14 | 0.365 | 0.458 | 0.532 | 0.661 |
| 15 | 0.351 | 0.441 | 0.514 | 0.641 |
| 16 | 0.338 | 0.426 | 0.497 | 0.623 |
| 17 | 0.327 | 0.412 | 0.482 | 0.606 |
| 18 | 0.317 | 0.400 | 0.468 | 0.590 |
| 19 | 0.308 | 0.389 | 0.456 | 0.575 |
| 20 | 0.299 | 0.378 | 0.444 | 0.561 |
| 21 | 0.291 | 0.369 | 0.433 | 0.549 |
| 22 | 0.284 | 0.360 | 0.423 | 0.537 |
| 23 | 0.277 | 0.352 | 0.413 | 0.526 |
| 24 | 0.271 | 0.344 | 0.404 | 0.515 |
| 25 | 0.265 | 0.337 | 0.396 | 0.505 |
| 26 | 0.260 | 0.330 | 0.388 | 0.496 |
| 27 | 0.255 | 0.323 | 0.381 | 0.487 |
| 28 | 0.250 | 0.317 | 0.374 | 0.479 |
| 29 | 0.245 | 0.311 | 0.367 | 0.471 |
| 30 | 0.241 | 0.306 | 0.361 | 0.463 |
| 40 | 0.207 | 0.264 | 0.312 | 0.403 |
| 50 | 0.184 | 0.235 | 0.279 | 0.361 |
| 60 | 0.168 | 0.214 | 0.254 | 0.330 |
| 70 | 0.155 | 0.198 | 0.235 | 0.306 |
| 80 | 0.145 | 0.185 | 0.220 | 0.286 |
| 90 | 0.136 | 0.174 | 0.207 | 0.270 |
| 100 | 0.129 | 0.165 | 0.197 | 0.256 |
| 200 | 0.091 | 0.117 | 0.139 | 0.182 |

## Table A10    The Spearman rank correlation coefficient

The table gives the critical values of the Spearman rank correlation coefficient, $\rho$, for different numbers of pairs of observations, $N$.

| | Significance level: two-tailed/non-directional | | | |
|---|---|---|---|---|
| | *0.20* | *0.10* | *0.05* | *0.01* |
| | Significance level: one-tailed/directional | | | |
| *N* | *0.10* | *0.05* | *0.025* | *0.005* |
| 5 | 0.800 | 0.900 | 1.000 | – |
| 6 | 0.657 | 0.829 | 0.886 | 1.000 |
| 7 | 0.571 | 0.714 | 0.786 | 0.929 |
| 8 | 0.524 | 0.643 | 0.738 | 0.881 |
| 9 | 0.483 | 0.600 | 0.700 | 0.833 |
| 10 | 0.455 | 0.564 | 0.648 | 0.794 |
| 11 | 0.427 | 0.536 | 0.618 | 0.755 |
| 12 | 0.406 | 0.503 | 0.587 | 0.727 |
| 13 | 0.385 | 0.484 | 0.560 | 0.703 |
| 14 | 0.367 | 0.464 | 0.538 | 0.679 |
| 15 | 0.354 | 0.446 | 0.521 | 0.654 |
| 16 | 0.341 | 0.429 | 0.503 | 0.635 |
| 17 | 0.328 | 0.414 | 0.488 | 0.618 |
| 18 | 0.317 | 0.401 | 0.472 | 0.600 |
| 19 | 0.309 | 0.391 | 0.460 | 0.584 |
| 20 | 0.299 | 0.380 | 0.447 | 0.570 |
| 21 | 0.292 | 0.370 | 0.436 | 0.556 |
| 22 | 0.284 | 0.361 | 0.425 | 0.544 |
| 23 | 0.278 | 0.353 | 0.416 | 0.532 |
| 24 | 0.271 | 0.344 | 0.407 | 0.521 |
| 25 | 0.265 | 0.337 | 0.398 | 0.511 |
| 26 | 0.259 | 0.331 | 0.390 | 0.501 |
| 27 | 0.255 | 0.324 | 0.383 | 0.492 |
| 28 | 0.250 | 0.318 | 0.375 | 0.483 |
| 29 | 0.245 | 0.312 | 0.368 | 0.475 |
| 30 | 0.240 | 0.306 | 0.362 | 0.467 |
| 35 | 0.222 | 0.283 | 0.335 | 0.433 |
| 40 | 0.207 | 0.264 | 0.313 | 0.405 |
| 45 | 0.194 | 0.248 | 0.294 | 0.382 |
| 50 | 0.184 | 0.235 | 0.279 | 0.363 |
| 55 | 0.175 | 0.224 | 0.266 | 0.346 |
| 60 | 0.168 | 0.214 | 0.255 | 0.331 |

# Appendix 2   Answers to exercises

*Note:* In numerical questions, where more than one example of a particular method is given, the later examples are not necessarily worked through in full detail.

## Chapter 1

2   (i)   Ratio: time scale has 'absolute zero'.
   (ii)   Ordinal: pleasantness scale cannot be assumed to have precisely equal intervals.
   (iii)   Nominal: either there is, or there is not, a finite verb.
   (iv)   Ordinal: we cannot claim equality of intervals between points on the grammaticality scale.
   (v)   Ratio: there is an 'absolute zero' (no sentences remembered correctly) and equality of intervals on the scale.

## Chapter 2

1   It will usually be found that word length distributions are positively skewed. The precise location of the peak of the curve may vary according to the nature of the text: for instance, certain types of written language have a high proportion of two-letter prepositions such as *in, on, of, at, to, by*, or a high proportion of two- and three-letter pronouns such as *we, me, us, she, him, her, you*.

2

| Intensity | Frequency | | | |
|---|---|---|---|---|
| | Stressed | | Unstressed | |
| 7-9 | | | / | 1 |
| 10-12 | | | / | 1 |
| 13-15 | | | ЖН / | 6 |
| 16-18 | /// | 3 | ЖН /// | 8 |
| 19-21 | ЖН ЖН ЖН //// | 19 | ЖН ЖН ЖН ЖН | 20 |
| 22-24 | ЖН ЖН ЖН ЖН ЖН /// | 28 | ЖН ЖН ЖН ЖН ЖН // | 27 |
| 25-27 | ЖН ЖН ЖН ЖН ЖН ЖН / | 31 | ЖН ЖН ЖН ЖН /// | 23 |
| 28-30 | ЖН ЖН //// | 14 | ЖН ЖН //// | 14 |
| 31-33 | ЖН | 5 | | |
| | | 100 | | 100 |

The polygons corresponding to these values show that the differences between the distributions are quite small, and this
corroborates the view that stress may not be a quantitatively
important phenomenon in French. Both curves are fairly
symmetrical about their highest point. The peak for stressed
syllables is at a slightly higher intensity than that for unstressed
syllables. The range of values is greater for the unstressed
syllables.

3

| Pause length (1/50 sec units) | Frequency |
|---|---|
| 0-5 | 34 |
| 6-10 | 23 |
| 11-15 | 11 |
| 16-20 | 12 |
| 21-25 | 31 |
| 26-30 | 20 |
| 31-35 | 14 |
| 36-40 | 4 |
| 41-45 | 1 |

The histogram will show two peaks, one at very low pause
lengths, the other at 21-25 time units, suggesting two func-
tionally different types of pause. The next stage of the investi-

gation would be to examine the environments of the pauses in each category, to see whether any generalisations could be made.

## Chapter 3

1  (iii)  Since the data are of the ratio type, and do not appear to contain any highly untypical values, the mean is an appropriate measure of central tendency.

$$\bar{x} = \frac{\Sigma x}{N} = \frac{602}{30} = 20.07 \text{ msec.}$$

$$s = \sqrt{\frac{\Sigma x^2 - (\Sigma x)^2/N}{N-1}} = \sqrt{\frac{12\,482 - 602^2/30}{29}}$$

$$= 3.72 \text{ msec.}$$

2  Since word length distributions are usually positively skewed, the median would be the most appropriate measure of central tendency in most cases.

3  The exact values calculated will depend on whether the raw data or grouped data have been used. The following calculations are based on the class intervals suggested in the answer to question 2 of chapter 2.

*Stressed syllables*

$$\bar{x} = \frac{\Sigma fx}{N}$$

where $f$ = frequency in a given class
      $x$ = mid-point of class interval

$$\bar{x} = \{(3 \times 17) + (19 \times 20) + (28 \times 23) + (31 \times 26)$$
$$+ (14 \times 29) + (5 \times 32)\}/100$$

$$= \frac{2\,447}{100} = 24.47 \text{ units}$$

($\bar{x}$ for raw data = 24.31 units)

Since there are 50 observations in the range up to 24 units, and 50 in the range from 25 units upwards, the median is the mid-point of the combined classes 22–24 and 25–27, i.e. 24.50 units. The mode is the 25–27 class, whose mid-point is at 26 units. The range is from the 16–18 class to the 31–33 class (from the raw data the range is from 16 to 31, i.e. 15 units). The standard deviation is given by:

$$s = \sqrt{\frac{\Sigma fx^2 - (\Sigma fx)^2/N}{N-1}} = \sqrt{\frac{61\,129 - 2\,447^2/100}{99}}$$

$$= 3.55 \text{ units.}$$

(for raw data also, $s = 3.55$ units).

*Unstressed syllables*

$$\bar{x} = \frac{\Sigma fx}{N} = \frac{2\,264}{100} = 22.64 \text{ units for grouped data}$$

($\bar{x} = 22.43$ units for raw data).

$$\text{median} = L + \left(\frac{N/2 - F}{f_\mathrm{m}}\right)h = 21.5 + \left(\frac{50-36}{27}\right) \times 3$$

$$= 23.06 \text{ units.}$$

mode = 22–24 class, mid-point 23 units

range = 7–9 to 28–30 (or 23 units from the raw data)

$$\text{standard deviation} = \sqrt{\frac{\Sigma fx^2 - (\Sigma fx)^2/N}{N-1}}$$

$$= \sqrt{\frac{53\,278 - 2\,264^2/100}{99}}$$

$$= 4.52 \text{ units, for grouped data}$$

($s = 4.39$ units for raw data).

These results confirm our conclusions from frequency polygons (question 2 in chapter 2): the measures of central tendency are slightly higher, but the variability is lower, for the stressed syllables. The mean, median and mode are close together, reflecting the symmetrical nature of the distribution.

4

|  | Experimental group | Control group |
|---|---|---|
| Mean | 38.60 | 38.60 |
| Standard deviation | 21.96 | 8.14 |

Although the average performance of the two groups is identical, the variability is much greater for the treated group than for the control group, suggesting that the treatment considerably improves the performance of some aphasics, but is deleterious to others.

5  The median is the most appropriate measure of central tendency, since the data are of the ordinal type. The frequency distributions are as follows:

Frequency for

| Politeness rating | Sentence 1 | Sentence 2 |
|---|---|---|
| 1 | 23 | 9 |
| 2 | 17 | 16 |
| 3 | 6 | 13 |
| 4 | 2 | 11 |
| 5 | 1 | 1 |
| 6 | 0 | 0 |
| 7 | 1 | 0 |

$$\text{median for sentence 1} = L + \left(\frac{N/2 - F}{f_\mathrm{m}}\right)h$$

$$= 1.5 + \left(\frac{50/2 - 23}{17}\right) \times 1$$

$$= 1.62.$$

Median for sentence 2 = 2.50, since there are 25 ratings of 1 or 2, and 25 of 3 or above, so that the median clearly lies half way between 2 and 3.

**Chapter 4**

1  (ii)  The histogram will be quite symmetrical.

$\bar{x} = 49.88$ marks

$s = 15.53$ marks

$\bar{x} \pm s = 49.88 \pm 15.53 = 34$ to $65$ marks

$\bar{x} \pm 2s = 49.88 \pm 31.06 = 19$ to $81$ marks

% of observations lying in range 34–65 marks
$$= 35/50 \times 100$$
$$= 70\%$$

% of observations lying in range 19–81 marks
$$= 48/50 \times 100$$
$$= 96\%.$$

Comparing these figures with those for the normal curve (68.2 and 95.4 per cent, respectively), we see that the data correspond closely to the predictions for a normal distribution.

(iii)  (a)  We have

$$z = \frac{x - \bar{x}}{s} = \frac{40 - 49.88}{15.53} = -0.64.$$

From table A2, 0.2611 of the area under the curve lies below this $z$ value. Thus, the proportion of marks expected to fall below 40 is 26.1 per cent.

(b)  For 60 marks, we have

$$z = \frac{60 - 49.88}{15.53} = 0.65.$$

From table A2, 0.2578 of area under curve lies above this value. For 70 marks,

$$z = \frac{70 - 49.88}{15.33} = 1.30.$$

0.0968 of area under curve lies above this. Thus, the proportion of marks expected to lie between 60 and 70 is

$$0.2578 - 0.0968 = 0.1610 = 16.1\%.$$

2   (i)   For 10 dB,

$$z = \frac{x - \bar{x}}{s} = \frac{10 - 23.4}{5.8} = -2.31.$$

The proportion lying below this is 0.0104, or 1.0 per cent.
(ii)   For 30 dB,

$$z = \frac{30 - 23.4}{5.8} = 1.14.$$

The proportion above this is 0.1271, or 12.7 per cent.
(iii)   For 20 dB,

$$z = \frac{20 - 23.4}{5.8} = -0.59.$$

The proportion below this is 0.2776. For 25 dB,

$$z = \frac{25 - 23.4}{5.8} = 0.28.$$

The proportion above this is 0.3897. Therefore the proportion between 20 dB and 25 dB is

$$1 - 0.2776 - 0.3897 = 0.3327 = 33.3\%.$$

3   (i)   The histogram is quite symmetrical.

(ii)      $\bar{x} = 53.30$ marks.

          $s = 16.62$ marks.

(iii)     $\bar{x} \pm s = 53.30 \pm 16.62 = 37$ to 70 marks.

          $\bar{x} \pm 2s = 53.30 \pm 33.24 = 20$ to 87 marks.

% in range 37–70 = 34/50 × 100 = 68%

% in range 20–87 = 47/50 × 100 = 94%.

The percentages agree very well with those for the normal distribution.

**Chapter 5**

1     standard error $= \dfrac{s}{\sqrt{N}} = \dfrac{6.87}{\sqrt{100}} = 0.69$ words.

The 95 per cent confidence limits are

$$\bar{x} \pm 1.96 \times \text{standard error} = 14.21 \pm (1.96 \times 0.69)$$
$$= 14.21 \pm 1.35$$
$$= 12.86 \text{ to } 15.56 \text{ words.}$$

2   (i)   $\bar{x} = 26.05$ msec.

    (ii)   $s = 6.26$ msec.

    (iii)   standard error $= 6.26/\sqrt{20} = 1.40$ msec.

    (iv)   Since the sample is small, the $t$ distribution must be used. From table A3, the critical value for the 5 per cent level and $(20-1) = 19$ df is 2.093. The 95 per cent confidence limits are thus given by

$$\bar{x} \pm 2.093 \times \text{standard error} = 26.05 \pm (2.093 \times 1.40)$$
$$= 26.05 \pm 2.93$$
$$= 23.12 \text{ to } 28.98 \text{ msec.}$$

The confidence limits are rather wide apart, because of the high standard deviation relative to the mean.

3   (i)   $\bar{x} = 0.51$ sec.

    (ii)   $s = 0.16$ sec.

    (iii)   standard error $= 0.16/\sqrt{30} = 0.03$ sec.

(iv)  99 per cent confidence limits are:

$$\bar{x} \pm 2.58 \times \text{standard error} = 0.51 \pm (2.58 \times 0.03)$$
$$= 0.51 \pm 0.08$$
$$= 0.43 \text{ to } 0.59 \text{ sec.}$$

4      proportion of auxiliaries $= p = 63/300 = 0.21$.

$$\text{standard error} = \sqrt{\frac{p(1-p)}{N}} = \sqrt{\frac{0.21(1-0.21)}{300}} = 0.02.$$

95 per cent confidence limits are:

$$p \pm 1.96 \times \text{standard error} = 0.21 \pm (1.96 \times 0.02)$$
$$= 0.21 \pm 0.04 = 0.17 \text{ to } 0.25$$
$$= 17\% \text{ to } 25\%$$

5      error tolerated $= 0.01 = 1.96 \times \text{standard error}$.

Thus

$$\text{standard error} = 0.01/1.96.$$

But

$$\text{standard error} = \sqrt{\frac{p(1-p)}{N}} \text{ and } p = 0.21 \text{ (from question 4)}$$

Therefore

$$\sqrt{\frac{0.21(1-0.21)}{N}} = \frac{0.01}{1.96}$$

$$\frac{0.21(1-0.21)}{N} = \left(\frac{0.01}{1.96}\right)^2$$

$$N = \frac{0.21(1-0.21)}{(0.01/1.96)^2} = 6373.$$

We thus need a sample of about 6 400 finite verbs to estimate the proportion of auxiliaries to within 1 per cent.

**Chapter 7**

1 (i) *Text A*

$\bar{x} = 311.00$ word types.

$s = 38.52$ word types.

standard error $= 38.52/\sqrt{50} = 5.45$ word types.

99 per cent confidence limits are:

$\bar{x} \pm 2.58 \times$ standard error $= 311.00 \pm (2.58 \times 5.45)$

$= 296.94$ to $325.06$ word types.

*Text B*

$\bar{x} = 346.64$ word types.

$s = 37.21$ word types.

standard error $= 37.21/\sqrt{50} = 5.26$ word types.

99 per cent confidence limits are:

$\bar{x} \pm 2.58 \times$ standard error $= 346.64 \pm (2.58 \times 5.26)$

$= 333.07$ to $360.21$ word types.

(ii) Since the samples are large, we can use the $z$-test.

$$z = \frac{\bar{x}_1 - \bar{x}_2}{\sqrt{\dfrac{s_1^2}{N_1} + \dfrac{s_2^2}{N_2}}} = \frac{311.00 - 346.64}{\sqrt{\dfrac{38.52^2}{50} + \dfrac{37.21^2}{50}}} = -4.71.$$

The critical value for $p \leqslant 0.01$ in a non-directional test is 2.58. The calculated value of $z$ (ignoring the sign) exceeds this. The means are therefore significantly different at the 1 per cent level.

2 Since the samples are small, a $t$-test must be used.

| | Group A | Group B |
|---|---|---|
| $\bar{x}$ | 51.36 | 47.33 |
| $s$ | 9.33 | 10.42 |

Note that the values of $s$, and hence the variances, are similar. The samples are really too small for any serious assessment of normality, but the following figures are at least consistent with a normal distribution:

| % in range | *Group A* | *Group B* |
|---|---|---|
| $\bar{x} \pm s$ | 64 | 67 |
| $\bar{x} \pm 2s$ | 100 | 100 |

$$t = \frac{\bar{x}_1 - \bar{x}_2}{\sqrt{s_p^2(1/N_1 + 1/N_2)}}$$

where

$$s_p^2 = \frac{\Sigma x_1^2 - (\Sigma x_1)^2/N_1 + \Sigma x_2^2 - (\Sigma x_2)^2/N_2}{N_1 + N_2 - 2}.$$

$$s_p^2 = \frac{29\,891 - 565^2/11 + 21\,032 - 426^2/9}{11 + 9 - 2} = 96.59.$$

$$t = \frac{51.36 - 47.33}{\sqrt{96.59(\frac{1}{11} + \frac{1}{9})}} = 0.91.$$

The critical value of $t$ for the 5 per cent level and $(11 + 9 - 2)$ = 18 df in a non-directional test is 2.101. Since the calculated value is lower than this, the means do not differ significantly at the 5 per cent level.

3   The $t$-test for correlated samples is appropriate here.

| *Pitch levels (arbitrary units) for:* | | | |
|---|---|---|---|
| *Sentence 1* | *Sentence 2* | *d* | *d²* |
| 30 | 27 | 3 | 9 |
| 41 | 36 | 5 | 25 |
| 34 | 35 | −1 | 1 |
| 28 | 30 | −2 | 4 |
| 35 | 38 | −3 | 9 |
| 39 | 44 | −5 | 25 |
| 40 | 46 | −6 | 36 |
| 29 | 31 | −2 | 4 |
| 27 | 33 | −6 | 36 |
| 33 | 37 | −4 | 16 |
| | | $\Sigma d = -21$ | $\Sigma d^2 = 165$ |

$$t = \frac{\Sigma d}{\sqrt{\frac{N\Sigma d^2 - (\Sigma d)^2}{N-1}}} = \frac{-21}{\sqrt{\frac{(10 \times 165) - (-21)^2}{10-1}}}$$

$$= \frac{-21}{\sqrt{\frac{1\,650 - 441}{9}}} = -1.81.$$

The critical value for $t$ for the 5 per cent level and 9 df in a directional test is 1.833. Since the calculated value for $t$ is lower than this, the means are not significantly different at the 5 per cent level.

4   Since the samples are small and the groups independent, the appropriate test is the $t$-test for independent samples. We shall assume normality and homogeneity of variance in the populations from which the samples are derived.

$$\bar{x}_1 = 53.2.$$
$$\bar{x}_2 = 60.1.$$
$$s_p^2 = \frac{28\,668 - 532^2/10 + 36\,575 - 601^2/10}{10 + 10 - 2} = 45.58.$$
$$t = \frac{53.2 - 60.1}{\sqrt{45.58(\frac{1}{10} + \frac{1}{10})}} = -2.29.$$

The critical value of $t$ for the 5 per cent level and 18 df in a directional test is 1.734. Since the calculated value of $t$ exceeds this, the means are significantly different at the 5 per cent level. Since $\bar{x}_1 > \bar{x}_2$, the difference is in the predicted direction.

5

$$z = \frac{p_1 - p_2}{\sqrt{p_p(1-p_p)\left(\frac{1}{N_1} + \frac{1}{N_2}\right)}}$$

where

$$p_p = \frac{f_1 + f_2}{N_1 + N_2}.$$

$$p_p = \frac{32 + 24}{100 + 100} = 0.28.$$

$$z = \frac{32/100 - 24/100}{\sqrt{0.28(1-0.28)(\frac{1}{100} + \frac{1}{100})}} = \frac{0.08}{\sqrt{0.0040}} = 1.26.$$

The critical value of $z$ for the 1 per cent level in a non-directional test is 2.58. Since the calculated value of $z$ is lower than this, we cannot claim that the proportions are significantly different at the 1 per cent level.

## Chapter 8

1   Since the data are probably best regarded as ordinal, and the groups are independent, the Mann–Whitney $U$-test is appropriate. We rank all the data in the combined groups, and then find the rank sum for the smaller group.

| Group 1 | Rank | Group 2 | Rank |
|:---:|:---:|:---:|:---:|
| 8 | 27 | 4 | 5.5 |
| 6 | 17 | 6 | 17 |
| 3 | 2 | 3 | 2 |
| 5 | 10.5 | 3 | 2 |
| 8 | 27 | 7 | 23 |
| 7 | 23 | 7 | 23 |
| 7 | 23 | 5 | 10.5 |
| 6 | 17 | 5 | 10.5 |
| 5 | 10.5 | 4 | 5.5 |
| 6 | 17 | 4 | 5.5 |
| 6 | 17 | 6 | 17 |
| 7 | 23 | 5 | 10.5 |
| 8 | 27 | 6 | 17 |
| | | 5 | 10.5 |
| | | 4 | 5.5 |
| | $R_1 = 241$ | | |

$$U_1 = N_1 N_2 + \frac{N_1(N_1 + 1)}{2} - R_1$$

$$= (13 \times 15) + \frac{13 \times 14}{2} - 241$$

$$= 195 + 91 - 241 = 45$$
$$U_2 = N_1 N_2 - U_1 = (13 \times 15) - 45 = 150$$
$$U = \text{smaller of } U_1 \text{ and } U_2 = 45.$$

The critical value of $U$ for the 2.5 per cent level in a directional test, with $N_1 = 13$ and $N_2 = 15$, is 54. The calculated value of $U$ is below the critical value, so we can claim a significant difference at the 2.5 per cent level. Since group 1 has more of the higher ranks (this could be confirmed by calculating the mean rank for each group), the difference is in the predicted direction.

2 Since the data are of the ratio type, and the sets correlated, the Wilcoxon signed-ranks test is appropriate. We take the differences between pairs of scores; rank them, omitting any zero differences; assign to each rank the sign of the difference it represents; and find the sums of positive and negative ranks.

| Set 1 | Set 2 | Difference | Rank |
|---|---|---|---|
| 8 | 5 | 3 | +18 |
| 7 | 7 | 0 | − |
| 4 | 9 | −5 | −23.5 |
| 7 | 3 | 4 | +21 |
| 6 | 4 | 2 | +11.5 |
| 5 | 5 | 0 | − |
| 2 | 0 | 2 | +11.5 |
| 6 | 4 | 2 | +11.5 |
| 9 | 7 | 2 | +11.5 |
| 8 | 6 | 2 | +11.5 |
| 10 | 5 | 5 | +23.5 |
| 5 | 6 | −1 | −3.5 |
| 4 | 3 | 1 | +3.5 |
| 10 | 9 | 1 | +3.5 |
| 8 | 10 | −2 | −11.5 |
| 4 | 4 | 0 | − |
| 7 | 5 | 2 | +11.5 |
| 8 | 6 | 2 | +11.5 |
| 6 | 6 | 0 | − |
| 5 | 2 | 3 | +18 |
| 8 | 7 | 1 | +3.5 |

| Set 1 | Set 2 | Difference | Rank |
|-------|-------|------------|------|
| 7 | 7 | 0 | – |
| 6 | 9 | −3 | −18 |
| 9 | 3 | 6 | +25 |
| 4 | 6 | −2 | −11.5 |
| 3 | 1 | 2 | +11.5 |
| 8 | 7 | 1 | +3.5 |
| 7 | 8 | −1 | −3.5 |
| 5 | 1 | 4 | +21 |
| 6 | 2 | 4 | +21 |

sum of positive ranks   = 253.5.

sum of negative ranks   = 71.5.

$W$ = smaller of the two = 71.5.

The critical value of $W$ for the 5 per cent level and 25 pairs of non-tied scores in a non-directional test is 89. Since the calculated value of $W$ lies below this, we can claim a significant difference between the two sets of scores at the 5 per cent level.

Since the number of pairs of scores is greater than 20, we can also use the $z$ approximation:

$$z = \frac{W - \dfrac{N(N+1)}{4}}{\sqrt{\dfrac{N(N+1)(2N+1)}{24}}} = \frac{71.5 - \dfrac{(25 \times 26)}{4}}{\sqrt{\dfrac{25 \times 26 \times 51}{24}}} = -2.45.$$

The critical value of $z$ for the 5 per cent level in a non-directional test is 1.96. Since the calculated value of $z$ (ignoring the sign) exceeds the critical value, we again conclude that a significant difference can be claimed at the 5 per cent level.

3   The data are ordinal and a repeated measures design is used. The sign test is therefore appropriate. We find the sign of the difference between each pair of scores, subtracting consistently.

| Sentence 1 | Sentence 2 | Sign of sentence 1 – sentence 2 |
|:---:|:---:|:---:|
| 1 | 3 | – |
| 2 | 2 | 0 |
| 1 | 4 | – |
| 2 | 3 | – |
| 3 | 1 | + |
| 2 | 4 | – |
| 1 | 1 | 0 |
| 2 | 3 | – |
| 3 | 5 | – |
| 1 | 3 | – |
| 2 | 3 | – |
| 1 | 4 | – |
| 2 | 1 | + |
| 2 | 4 | – |
| 1 | 3 | – |

There are 13 pairs of non-zero differences, 2 with the less frequent (positive) sign. Thus $x = 2$. The critical value of $x$ for the 5 per cent level and for 13 pairs in a directional test is 3. Since the calculated value of $x$ is smaller than the critical value, we may claim a significant difference at the 5 per cent level. Since the ratings for sentence 2 are higher than those for sentence 1 in 11 out of 15 cases, the differences are clearly in the predicted direction.

4 The data are ordinal and the groups independent. The Mann–Whitney $U$-test is therefore appropriate.

rank sum for method A $(R_1) = 182.5$

$U_1 = 162.5$

$U_2 = 62.5$

$U$ = smaller of the two $U$ values = 62.5

Critical value for $U$ for the 5 per cent level and $N_1 = N_2 = 15$ in a non-directional test is 64. Since the calculated value of $U$ is smaller than the critical value, we can claim significance at the 5 per cent level. The ranks for method B are higher overall.

**Chapter 9**

1    In the contingency table below, the calculated expected values are given in brackets.

| Word length (letters) | Frequency in The Colossus | Frequency in Winter Trees | Total |
|---|---|---|---|
| 1-3 | 3 473 (3 701.3) | 3 000 (2 771.7) | 6 473 |
| 4-6 | 3 743 (3 669.3) | 2 674 (2 747.1) | 6 417 |
| 7-9 | 1 272 (1 157.9) | 753 (867.1) | 2 025 |
| 10-12 | 285 (257.3) | 165 (192.7) | 450 |
| >12 | 54 (41.2) | 18 (30.8) | 72 |
| | 8 827 | 6 610 | 15 437 |

$$\chi^2 = \frac{(3\,473 - 3\,701.3)^2}{3\,701.3} + \frac{(3\,743 - 3\,669.3)^2}{3\,669.3} + \cdots \text{(etc.)}$$

$$= 78.86$$

$$df = (5 - 1)(2 - 1) = 4.$$

The critical value of $\chi^2$ for the 5 per cent level and 4 df is 9.49. There is therefore a significant difference in the word length distributions at the 5 per cent level (and indeed even at the 0.1 per cent level).

2

| | The Colossus | Crossing the Water | Ariel | Winter Trees | Total |
|---|---|---|---|---|---|
| *black* | 27 (34.3) | 28 (30.8) | 46 (36.2) | 26 (25.7) | 127 |
| other words | 8 800 (8 792.7) | 7 921 (7 918.2) | 9 294 (9 303.8) | 6 584 (6 584.3) | 32 599 |
| | 8 827 | 7 949 | 9 340 | 6 610 | 32 726 |

$\chi^2 = 4.48$.

The critical value of $\chi^2$ for the 5 per cent level with 3 df is 7.82. We cannot reject the null hypothesis of even distribution of items containing *black*.

3

| Punctuation mark | $\chi^2$ | df | Critical value | Significant at 5% level |
|---|---|---|---|---|
| Full stop | 19.20 | 3 | 7.82 | Yes |
| Comma | 26.50 | 3 | 7.82 | Yes |
| Colon | 32.40 | 3 | 7.82 | Yes |
| Semi-colon | 7.90 | 3 | 7.82 | Yes |
| Exclamation mark | 39.09 | 3 | 7.82 | Yes |
| Question mark | 86.25 | 3 | 7.82 | Yes |
| Dash | 19.15 | 3 | 7.82 | Yes |

Examination of the appropriate contingency tables will reveal that the earliest volume of poetry (*The Colossus*) has a higher proportion of the more 'formal' punctuation marks (colon, semi-colon) than expected on the basis of even distribution, while the last two volumes (*Ariel* and *Winter Trees*) have fewer of these punctuation marks than expected. On the other hand, the later volumes have more of the less formal punctuation marks (exclamation mark, question mark, dash, comma) than expected, whereas the earliest volume has fewer than expected. *Crossing the Water* appears to be transitional in terms of its punctuation. These results support the author's general hypothesis that the language becomes less formal as we go from early to later works.

4   $\chi^2 = 134.63$.

The critical value of $\chi^2$ for the 5 per cent level and $(9-1)(4-1)$ or 24 df is 36.42. We can thus claim a significant difference in the distribution of sentence length for the four texts. By considering the observed and expected frequencies in the contingency table, it is possible to show that *The Colossus* has fewer short sentences, and more long sentences, than expected for an even distribution, while *Winter Trees* has many more short sentences, and fewer long ones, than expected. *Crossing the Water* and *Ariel* have a low proportion of very short sentences (1–5 words) and very long sentences (>35 words), and appear to be transitional between the other two volumes. Overall, the results tend to confirm the conclusions drawn from punctuation studies: there seems to be a decrease in formal complexity from earlier to later works, reflecting a structurally simpler and less formal style.

5    To avoid cells with expected frequencies of <5, we group the data from question 2 of the chapter 2 exercises as shown in tables A2.1 and A2.2.

*Stressed syllables*

$\bar{x} = 24.47$ units, $s = 3.55$ units, from question 3 of the exercises to chapter 3.

There are 4 pairs of $E$ and $O$ values, but the distributions have been made to agree on 3 values (those of the sample size, mean and standard deviation), so that df $= 4 - 3 = 1$. The critical value at the 5 per cent level is 3.84. Since the calculated value of $\chi^2$ is smaller than this, we cannot reject the null hypothesis that the data are normally distributed.

*Unstressed syllables*

$\bar{x} = 22.64$ units, $s = 4.52$ units, from question 3 of the exercises to chapter 3.

Number of df $= 5 - 3 = 2$. The critical value at the 5 per cent level is 5.99. Since the calculated value is smaller than this, we cannot reject the null hypothesis that the data are normally distributed.

6    *must*:

|  | British | American | Total |
|---|---|---|---|
| root | 153 | 150 | 303 |
| epistemic | 74 | 47 | 121 |
|  | 227 | 197 | 424 |

**Table A2.1**

| Intensity | Frequency (O) | Upper limit | Deviation from $\bar{x}$ | $z = \dfrac{deviation}{s}$ | Proportion below boundary | Proportion within class | E | $\dfrac{(O-E)^2}{E}$ |
|---|---|---|---|---|---|---|---|---|
| ≤21 | 22 | 21.50 | −2.97 | −0.84 | 0.201 | 0.201 | 20.1 | 0.18 |
| 22–24 | 28 | 24.50 | 0.03 | 0.01 | 0.504 | 0.303 | 30.3 | 0.17 |
| 25–27 | 31 | 27.50 | 3.03 | 0.85 | 0.802 | 0.298 | 29.8 | 0.05 |
| ≥28 | 19 | | | | 1.000 | 0.198 | 19.8 | 0.03 |
| | | | | | | 1.000 | 100.0 | $\chi^2 = 0.43$ |

**Table A2.2**

| Intensity | Frequency (O) | Upper limit | Deviation from $\bar{x}$ | $z = \dfrac{deviation}{s}$ | Proportion below boundary | Proportion within class | E | $\dfrac{(O-E)^2}{E}$ |
|---|---|---|---|---|---|---|---|---|
| ≤18 | 16 | 18.50 | −4.14 | −0.92 | 0.179 | 0.179 | 17.9 | 0.20 |
| 19–21 | 20 | 21.50 | −1.14 | −0.25 | 0.401 | 0.222 | 22.2 | 0.22 |
| 22–24 | 27 | 24.50 | 1.86 | 0.41 | 0.659 | 0.258 | 25.8 | 0.06 |
| 25–27 | 23 | 27.50 | 4.86 | 1.08 | 0.860 | 0.201 | 20.1 | 0.42 |
| ≥28 | 14 | | | | 1.000 | 0.140 | 14.0 | 0.00 |
| | | | | | | 1.000 | 100.0 | $\chi^2 = 0.90$ |

Using Yates's correction,

$$\chi^2 = \frac{424\{|(150 \times 74) - (153 \times 47)|\} - 424/2)^2}{227 \times 197 \times 121 \times 303} = 3.53.$$

Without Yates's correction,

$$\chi^2 = \frac{424\{(150 \times 74) - (153 \times 47)\}^2}{227 \times 197 \times 121 \times 303} = 3.95.$$

The critical value of $\chi^2$ for 1 df at the 5 per cent level is 3.84. The $\chi^2$ value obtained without Yates's correction is thus just significant at the 5 per cent level, while that obtained using Yates's correction just fails to achieve significance.

*have to:'*

|  | British | American | Total |
|---|---|---|---|
| root | 226 | 209 | 435 |
| epistemic | 2 | 9 | 11 |
|  | 228 | 218 | 446 |

Using Yates's correction,

$$\chi^2 = \frac{446\{|(226 \times 9) - (209 \times 2)|\} - 446/2)^2}{228 \times 218 \times 11 \times 435} = 3.64.$$

Without Yates's correction,

$$\chi^2 = \frac{446\{(226 \times 9) - (209 \times 2)\}^2}{228 \times 218 \times 11 \times 435} = 4.90.$$

Again, the result from the uncorrected $\chi^2$ is significant at the 5 per cent level, but that from the corrected calculation is not quite significant.

7　(i)　$\chi^2$ for variation within the Early Middle English texts = 5.18;

　　　　$\chi^2$ for variation within the Late Middle English texts = 3.30.

The critical value of $\chi^2$ for 2 df at the 5 per cent level is 5.99, so that neither result is significant. That is, there is no significant difference in the distribution of contiguity of the predicator and following major element, across texts *within* either group.

Pooling the frequencies gives the following contingency table:

|  | *Early ME* | *Late ME* | *Total* |
| --- | --- | --- | --- |
| Non-contiguous | 75 | 66 | 141 |
| Contiguous | 455 | 534 | 989 |
|  | 530 | 600 | 1 130 |

$\chi^2$ (using Yates's correction) = 2.28.

The critical value for 1 df at the 5 per cent level is 3.84, so the difference in distribution *between* the two groups of texts is not significant. That is, no diachronic change in contiguity relations from Early to Late ME can be demonstrated.

(ii)  $\chi^2$ for Early ME texts = 7.38;
$\chi^2$ for Late ME texts = 2.68.

The critical value for 2 df at the 5 per cent level is 5.99, so that the variation within the Early ME texts is significant, whereas that in the Late ME texts is not. There is thus a diachronic change towards greater homogeneity on this measure.

(iii)  $\chi^2$ for Early ME texts = 0.13;
$\chi^2$ for Late ME texts = 11.87.

The critical value for 2 df at the 5 per cent level is 5.99, so that the variation within the Early ME texts is non-significant, but that in the Late ME texts is significant. We thus have the opposite situation to that in (ii): with respect to inversion of subject and verb after an introductory adverbial, there is a diachronic change towards greater heterogeneity.

**Chapter 10**

1    The standard deviations of the samples were calculated in question 3 of chapter 3, the results being as follows:

Stressed:    $s = 3.55$ units          $\therefore$ variance $= s^2 = 12.60$
$\qquad\qquad\qquad\qquad\qquad\qquad\qquad\qquad$ df $= 99$.

Unstressed: $s = 4.52$ units          $\therefore$ variance $= s^2 = 20.43$
$\qquad\qquad\qquad\qquad\qquad\qquad\qquad\qquad$ df $= 99$.

$$F = \frac{\text{larger variance}}{\text{smaller variance}} = \frac{20.43}{12.60} = 1.62.$$

The critical value of $F$ for the 10 per cent level in a non-directional test with 100 df for the smaller variance and 50 df for the larger variance is given in table A8 as 1.48. With $\infty$ df for the larger estimate it is 1.28. The critical value with 99 df for each variance estimate thus clearly lies between 1.28 and 1.48. The calculated value of $F$ exceeds this, and we can therefore reject the null hypothesis of homogeneity of variance at the 10 per cent level.

2    In question 1 of chapter 7, we calculated the values of $s$:

For text A: $s = 38.52$ word types   $\therefore$ variance $= s^2 = 1\,483.8$
$\qquad\qquad\qquad\qquad\qquad\qquad\qquad\qquad\qquad$ df $= 49$.

For text B: $s = 37.21$ word types   $\therefore$ variance $= s^2 = 1\,384.6$
$\qquad\qquad\qquad\qquad\qquad\qquad\qquad\qquad\qquad$ df $= 49$.

$$F = \frac{1\,483.8}{1\,384.6} = 1.07.$$

The critical value of $F$ for the 10 per cent level with 50 df for each estimate is 1.60 in a non-directional test. We therefore cannot reject the null hypothesis that the variances are equal.

3    Set A:          $\Sigma x_A = 123$    $\Sigma x_A^2 = 1\,979$    $N_A = 8$

Set B:          $\Sigma x_B = 394$    $\Sigma x_B^2 = 5\,612$    $N_A = 29$

Set C:          $\Sigma x_C = 968$    $\Sigma x_C^2 = 19\,534$    $N_C = 50$

Set D:          $\Sigma x_D = 274$    $\Sigma x_D^2 = 4\,510$    $N_D = 17$

For whole data set: $\Sigma x = 1\,759$   $\Sigma x^2 = 31\,635$   $N = 104$.

total sum of squares, $SS_t = \Sigma x^2 - \dfrac{(\Sigma x)^2}{N}$

$$= 31\,635 - \dfrac{(1\,759)^2}{104} = 1\,884.22.$$

between-groups sum of squares,

$$SS_b = \dfrac{(\Sigma x_A)^2}{N_A} + \dfrac{(\Sigma x_B)^2}{N_B} + \dfrac{(\Sigma x_C)^2}{N_C} + \dfrac{(\Sigma x_D)^2}{N_D} - \dfrac{(\Sigma x)^2}{N}$$

$$= 1\,891.13 + 5\,352.97 + 18\,740.48$$
$$+ 4\,416.24 - 29\,750.78$$
$$= 650.04.$$

within-groups sum of squares, $SS_w = SS_t - SS_b$

$$= 1\,884.22 - 650.04$$
$$= 1\,234.18.$$

between-groups mean square, $s_b^2 = \dfrac{SS_b}{k-1}$ ($k$ = no. of groups)

$$= \dfrac{650.04}{3} = 216.68.$$

within-groups mean square, $s_w^2 = \dfrac{SS_w}{N-k} = \dfrac{1\,234.18}{104-4} = 12.34.$

$$F = \dfrac{s_b^2}{s_w^2} = \dfrac{216.68}{12.34} = 17.56.$$

The critical value of $F$ at the 5 per cent level, with 3 df for $s_b^2$ and 100 df for $s_w^2$ is 2.70, in a directional test. Since the calculated value of $F$ exceeds the critical value, the means of the groups differ significantly at the 5 per cent level.

4   Let German = group 1, Japanese = group 2, French = group 3, Russian = group 4.

$\Sigma x_1 = 38$     $\Sigma x_1^2 = 184$     $N_1 = 10$     $\bar{x}_1 = 3.80$

$\Sigma x_2 = 60$     $\Sigma x_2^2 = 466$     $N_2 = 9$     $\bar{x}_2 = 6.67$

$$\Sigma x_3 = 42 \qquad \Sigma x_3^2 = 216 \qquad N_3 = 11 \qquad \bar{x}_3 = 3.82$$

$$\Sigma x_4 = 58 \qquad \Sigma x_4^2 = 464 \qquad N_4 = 8 \qquad \bar{x}_4 = 7.25$$

$$\Sigma x = 198 \qquad \Sigma x^2 = 1\,330 \qquad N = 38$$

$$SS_t = 298.32$$

$$SS_b = 93.58$$

$$SS_w = 204.74$$

$$s_b^2 = 31.19$$

$$s_w^2 = 6.02$$

$$F = 5.18$$

The critical value of $F$ at the 5 per cent level, with 3 df for $s_b^2$ and 35 df for $s_w^2$ (the nearest, in table A8, to the actual 34 df), is 2.87. There is thus a significant difference in the means of the groups at the 5 per cent level.

*Pairwise t-tests (non-directional)*

| Groups compared | $t$ value | df | Critical value at 5% level | Significant |
|---|---|---|---|---|
| German and Japanese | 2.51 | 17 | 2.110 | Yes |
| German and French | 0.02 | 19 | 2.093 | No |
| German and Russian | 3.19 | 16 | 2.120 | Yes |
| Japanese and French | 2.44 | 18 | 2.101 | Yes |
| Japanese and Russian | 0.44 | 15 | 2.131 | No |
| French and Russian | 3.06 | 17 | 2.110 | Yes |

## Chapter 11

1 If $x$ is the score for one learner on the French test, and $y$ the score on the German test,

$$\Sigma x = 1\,089 \qquad \Sigma y = 1\,065 \qquad \Sigma x^2 = 62\,795$$
$$\Sigma y^2 = 58\,957 \qquad \Sigma xy = 59\,918.$$

$$r = \frac{N\Sigma xy - \Sigma x \Sigma y}{\sqrt{\{N\Sigma x^2 - (\Sigma x)^2\}\{N\Sigma y^2 - (\Sigma y)^2\}}}$$

$$= \frac{(20 \times 59\,918) - (1\,089 \times 1\,065)}{\sqrt{\{(20 \times 62\,795) - 1\,089^2\}\{20 \times 58\,957) - 1\,065^2\}}}$$

$$= 0.69.$$

The critical value of $r$ for $N = 20$ at the 5 per cent level in a non-directional test is 0.444. There is thus a significant positive correlation between the two sets of scores.

2 Since the data are best regarded as ordinal, the Spearman rank correlation coefficient is the appropriate measure.

| Reading score | Rank | Writing score | Rank | d | $d^2$ |
|---|---|---|---|---|---|
| 3 | 4.5 | 6 | 13.5 | 9 | 81 |
| 4 | 8 | 4 | 8.5 | 0.5 | 0.25 |
| 5 | 11 | 3 | 4.5 | −6.5 | 42.25 |
| 6 | 13.5 | 7 | 15 | 1.5 | 2.25 |
| 3 | 4.5 | 4 | 8.5 | 4 | 16 |
| 4 | 8 | 2 | 1.5 | −6.5 | 42.25 |
| 3 | 4.5 | 5 | 11.5 | 7 | 49 |
| 5 | 11 | 6 | 13.5 | 2.5 | 6.25 |
| 2 | 1.5 | 3 | 4.5 | 3 | 9 |
| 4 | 8 | 5 | 11.5 | 3.5 | 12.25 |
| 7 | 15 | 3 | 4.5 | −10.5 | 110.25 |
| 5 | 11 | 4 | 8.5 | −2.5 | 6.25 |
| 6 | 13.5 | 4 | 8.5 | −5 | 25 |
| 2 | 1.5 | 3 | 4.5 | 3 | 9 |
| 3 | 4.5 | 2 | 1.5 | −3 | 9 |
| | | | | | $\Sigma d^2 = 420$ |

$$\rho = 1 - \frac{6\Sigma d^2}{N(N^2 - 1)} = 1 - \frac{6 \times 420}{15(15^2 - 1)} = 0.25.$$

The critical value of $\rho$ for $N = 15$ at the 5 per cent level in a non-directional test is 0.521. No significant correlation can therefore be claimed at the 5 per cent level.

3 *Order*

The scattergram indicates negative correlation. If $x$ = % order, $y$ = median politeness rating, then

$$\Sigma x = 1\,115 \qquad \Sigma y = 114.82 \qquad \Sigma x^2 = 70\,983$$

$$\Sigma y^2 = 477.67 \qquad \Sigma xy = 2\,186.6$$

$$N = 35$$

$$r = -0.78.$$

The critical value of $r$ at the 5 per cent level in a directional test is 0.306 for $N = 30$ and 0.264 for $N = 40$, as given in table A9. The calculated value of $r$ is thus clearly significant at the 5 per cent level.

*Request*

The scattergram indicates positive correlation. If $x$ = % request, $y$ = median politeness rating, then

$$\Sigma x = 1\,428 \qquad \Sigma y = 114.82 \qquad \Sigma x^2 = 98\,074$$

$$\Sigma y^2 = 477.67 \qquad \Sigma xy = 6\,435.07$$

$$N = 35$$

$$r = 0.87$$

The critical value of $r$ lies between 0.264 and 0.306, as shown above. The correlation is thus significant at the 5 per cent level.

*Suggestion*

The scattergram indicates no clear pattern of correlation. If $x$ = % suggestion, $y$ = median politeness rating, then

$$\Sigma x = 722 \qquad \Sigma y = 114.82 \qquad \Sigma x^2 = 36\,066$$

$$\Sigma y^2 = 477.67 \qquad \Sigma xy = 2\,231.60$$

$$N = 35$$

$$r = -0.09$$

The critical value is as before, and the calculated $r$ value is clearly non-significant.

4  *Language use and reading*

$$\Sigma d^2 = 804$$

$$\rho = 0.40$$

The critical value of $\rho$ for $N = 20$ at the 5 per cent level in a non-directional test is 0.447. The correlation between language use and reading ability is thus not significant at the 5 per cent level.

*Language use and social class*

$$\Sigma d^2 = 728.5$$

$$\rho = 0.45$$

The critical value is 0.447 as before. The correlation between language use and social class is thus just significant at the 5 per cent level.

*Reading and social class*

$$\Sigma d^2 = 571.5$$

$$\rho = 0.57$$

The critical value is again 0.447. There is thus a significant correlation between reading ability and social class at the 5 per cent level.

5

|  |  | *Predominantly use postvocalic /r/* | | |
|  |  | − | + | *Total* |
| --- | --- | --- | --- | --- |
| Male | + | 36 | 24 | 60 |
|  | − | 11 | 29 | 40 |
|  |  | 47 | 53 | 100 |

$$\phi = \frac{(24 \times 11) - (36 \times 29)}{47 \times 53 \times 40 \times 60} = -0.32$$

$$\chi^2 = N\phi^2 = 10.18.$$

The critical value of $\chi^2$ at the 5 per cent level for 1 df is 3.84. There is thus a significant correlation between sex and the use of postvocalic /r/. In the sample investigated, females use this feature more than males.

# References

Butler, C. S. (1979). Poetry and the computer: some quantitative aspects of the style of Sylvia Plath. *Proceedings of the British Academy*, LXV, 291–312.

Butler, C. S. (1982). *The Directive Function of the English Modals*. Unpublished PhD thesis, University of Nottingham.

Butler, C. S. (1985). *Computers in Linguistics*. Oxford: Basil Blackwell.

Coates, J. and Leech, G. (1980). The meanings of the modals in modern British and American English. *York Papers in Linguistics*, 8, 23–34.

Connolly, J. (1979). Quantitative analysis of syntactic change. *Nottingham Linguistic Circular*, 8/2, 108–18.

Ferguson, G. A. (1981). *Statistical Analysis in Psychology and Education* (5th edn). Tokyo: McGraw-Hill Kogakusha.

Meddis, R. (1984). *Statistics Using Ranks: a Unified Approach*. Oxford: Basil Blackwell.

Norušis, M. J. (1982). *SPSS Introductory Guide: Basic Statistics and Operations*. New York: McGraw-Hill.

Ryan, T. A. Jr, Joiner, B. L. and Ryan, B. F. (1976). *Minitab Student Handbook*. Boston, Mass.: Duxbury Press.

Wells, G. (1977). Language use and educational success: A response to Joan Tough's *The Development of Meaning* (1977). *Research in Education*, 18, 9–34.

# Index